ROCK
& POP

DRUMS

TRINITY
COLLEGE LONDON

THE EXAM AT A GLANCE

For your Rock & Pop exam you will need to perform a set of **three songs** and one of the **Session skills** assessments, either **Playback** or **Improvising**. You can choose the order in which you play your set-list.

Song 1

Choose a song from this book

OR from www.trinityrock.com

Song 2

Choose a different song from this book

OR from www.trinityrock.com

OR perform a song you have chosen yourself: this could be your own cover version or a song you have written. It should be at the same level as the songs in this book. See the website for detailed requirements.

Song 3: Technical focus

Choose one of the Technical focus songs from this book, which cover three specific technical elements.

Session skills

Choose either **Playback** or **Improvising**.

When you are preparing for your exam please check on **www.trinityrock.com** for the most up-to-date information and requirements as these can change from time to time.

CONTENTS

Each song has two backing tracks: the first includes a click track to play along with, the second omits the click track.

Trinity College London's Rock & Pop syllabus and supporting publications have been devised and produced in association with Faber Music and Peters Edition London.

Trinity College London
Registered office:
89 Albert Embankment
London SE1 7TP UK
T + 44 (0)20 7820 6100
F + 44 (0)20 7820 6161
E music@trinitycollege.co.uk
www.trinitycollege.co.uk

Registered in the UK. Company no. 02683033
Charity no. 1014792
Patron HRH The Duke of Kent KG

Copyright © 2012 Trinity College London
First published in 2012 by Trinity College London

Second impression, July 2012

Cover and book design by Chloë Alexander
Brand development by Andy Ashburner @ Caffeinehit (www.caffeinehit.com)
Photographs courtesy of Rex Features Limited.
Printed in England by Caligraving Ltd

Audio produced, mixed and mastered by Tom Fleming
Drums arranged by George Double
Backing tracks arranged by Tom Fleming
Musicians
Vocals: Bo Walton, Brendan Reilly & Alison Symons
Keyboards: Oliver Weeks
Guitar: Tom Fleming
Bass: Ben Hillyard
Drums: George Double
Studio Engineer: Joel Davies www.thelimehouse.com

All rights reserved

ISBN: 978-0-85736-250-6

SONGS MY GENERATION

TRACK 1 — demo

TRACK 2-3 — backing
2 with click
3 without click

The Who
Words and Music by Pete Townshend

♩ = 188 **Fast Rock** *2 bars count-in*

vocal cue
"My generation..."

Bass break

Outro

Drum solo over vamp

Repeat 4 times

SONGS PRIMITIVE NOTION

New Order
Words and Music by Stephen Morris, Peter Hook, Bernard Sumner and Gillian Gilbert

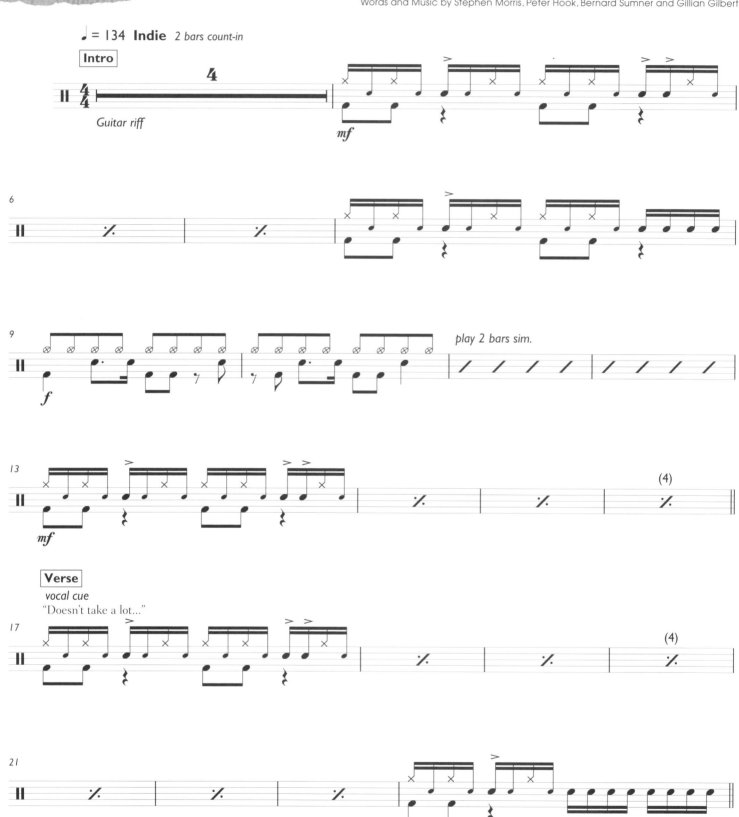

vocal cue
"If you hold a primitive notion..."

vocal cue
"Drink this magic potion..."

vocal cue
"Done it before..."

vocal cue
"How can it be..."

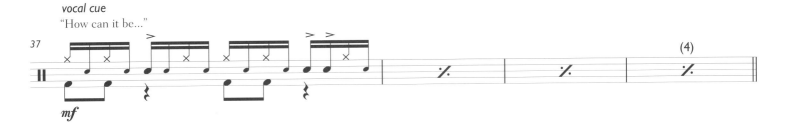

Drum Solo

continue solo over riff with *ad. lib.* fills

SONGS WOULD?

Alice In Chains
Words and Music by Jerry Cantrell

♩ = 100 **Grunge Rock** *2 bars count-in*

Intro

Verses *vocal cues*
1. "Know me…"
2. "Drifting…"

Hats slightly open

Chorus *vocal cue*
"Into the flood again…"

Ride

vocal cue
"So I made a big mistake…"

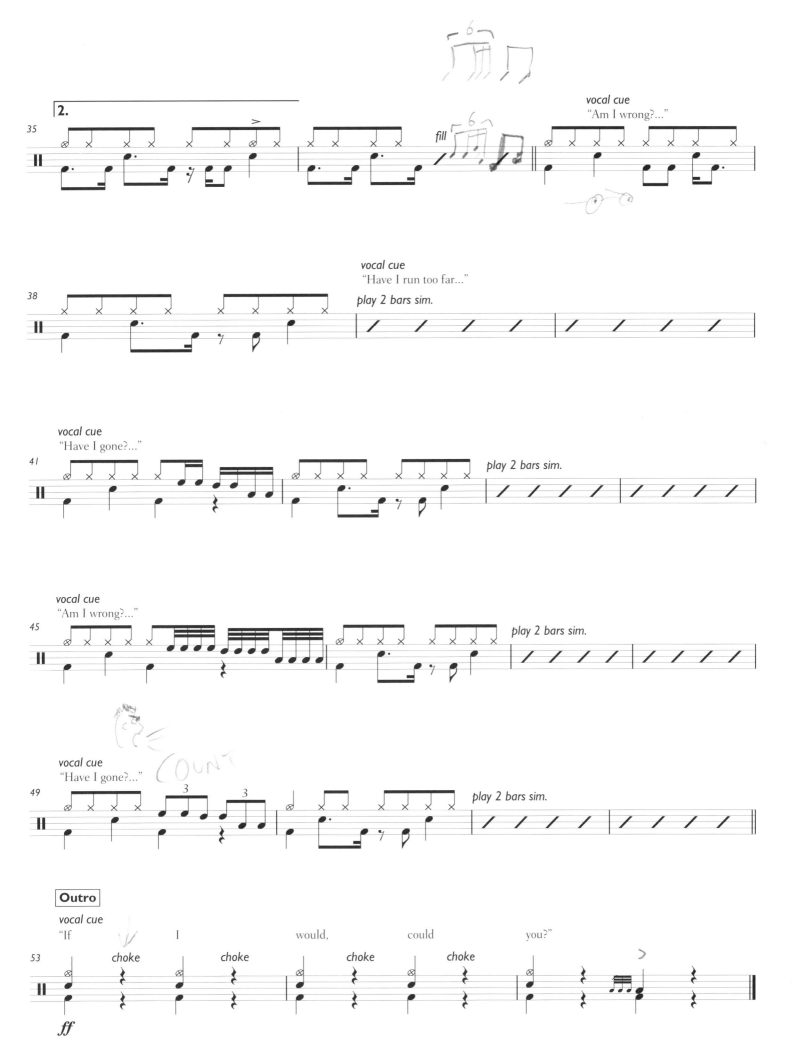

SONGS THE RAGGLE TAGGLE GYPSIES

TRACK 10 demo
TRACK 11-12 backing
11 with click
12 without click

Trad.
Words and Music Trad.

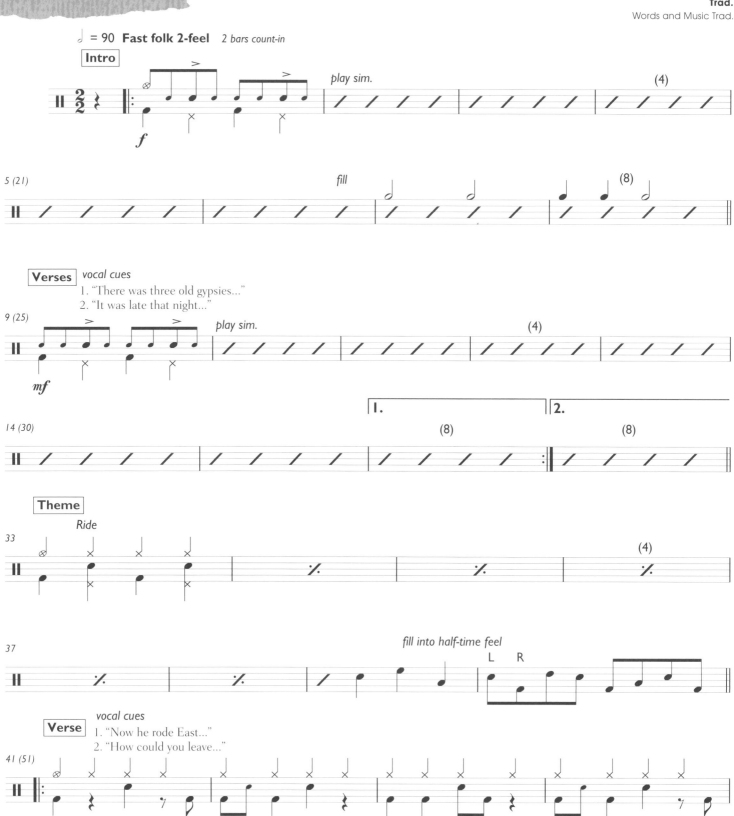

♩ = 90 **Fast folk 2-feel**   *2 bars count-in*

www.trinityrock.com

TECHNICAL FOCUS SONGS

The technical focus elements are listed after this song (on page 14), to avoid a page turn in the music.

TRACK 13 demo
TRACK 14-15 backing
14 with click
15 without click

AIRBAG

Radiohead
Words and Music by Thomas Yorke, Colin Greenwood, Edward O'Brien, Philip Selway and Jonathan Greenwood

Verse 2

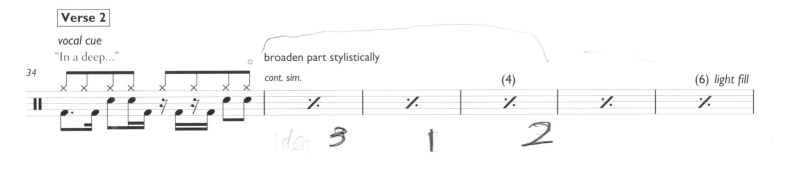

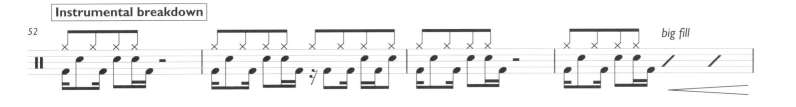

Instrumental breakdown

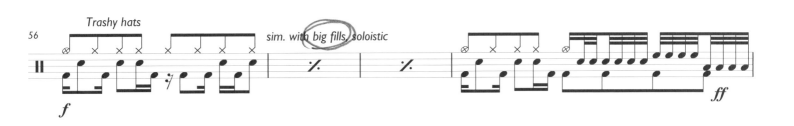

AIRBAG

In your exam, you will be assessed on the following technical elements:

1 Hand and foot co-ordination

The groove of this arrangement relies on the independence of bass and snare drum throughout. At 80 bpm, it is possible – and sensible – to count the ♪ pulse in your head as you play. The open hi-hat notes (in bar 8, for example) add another layer which needs careful co-ordination. Be sure to close the hi-hats exactly on the following ♪.

2 Drum break

Bars 26–33 are marked 'groove-based drum break over guitar chords'. You should base your playing around the groove, but also be expressive and inventive – filling out the sound and creating excitement. The best type of groove will be musically fluent whilst keeping an awareness of the style. Try to achieve a balanced range of dynamics and keep your rhythms tight. Consider how you are using the various sounds at your disposal to play a really consistent groove with a sense of feeling.

3 Rhythmic control

The instrumental breakdown section is rhythmically complex. It uses syncopation and ♪ notes. The syncopation is formed by placing notes on the weaker second and fourth ♪ of the bar. Make sure that your ♪ notes on hi-hat are really secure and place the syncopation around them.

WHITE ROOM

In your exam, you will be assessed on the following technical elements:

1 Ghost notes

'White Room' uses ghost notes in the main groove. Ghost notes are much softer, decorative sounds. When playing these strokes, almost drop the stick from a very shallow height, no more than an inch or so above the batter head. Be aware of the contrast between how high you lift your sticks when playing ghost notes and the height of your full strokes.

2 Buzzes

The buzzes in the groove should have a firm attack and be pressed tightly into the head to produce a short and clipped stroke. You will need to allow the stick some freedom of movement in your hand so that it is able to bounce when pressed on to the drum skin. Try to combine lots of bounces into a short sound to achieve the correct buzz effect.

3 Fills

Bars 53–60 of this song include fills. Judging what, how much and how loudly to play fills is one of the greatest challenges to any drummer. Always stay within the style and feel of the song. You could base your fills on some of those from earlier in the song – for example, ♩♩♩ (from bars 13 and 48) and ♩♩♩ (from bars 25 and 52).

TECHNICAL FOCUS SONGS

WHITE ROOM

TRACK 16 — demo
TRACK 17-18 — backing
17 with click
18 without click

Cream
Words and Music by Jack Bruce and Peter Brown

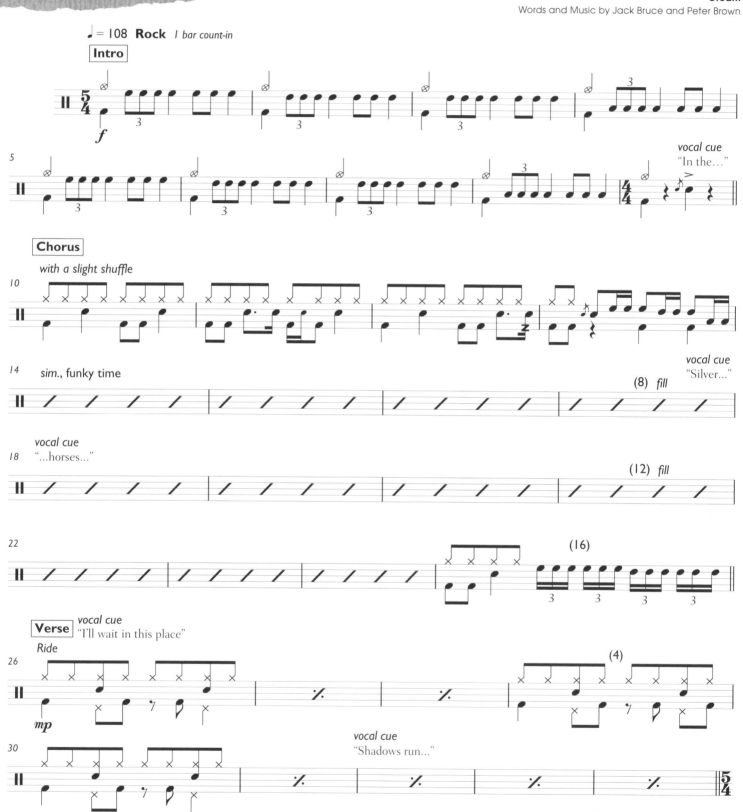

♩ = 108 **Rock** *1 bar count-in*

Intro

Chorus

with a slight shuffle

sim., funky time

vocal cue "...horses..."

vocal cue "Silver..."

(8) fill

(12) fill

(16)

Verse
vocal cue "I'll wait in this place"
Ride

(4)

vocal cue "Shadows run..."

www.trinityrock.com

MY GENERATION

The Who

The Who first got together as a band in 1963. Their stage act was loud and wild – when they played live, their great fortresses of amps made them one of the loudest bands around. During the 1960s, there was much talk of the generation gap between parents and their teenage offspring: 'My Generation', which includes the famous line 'I hope I die before I get old', captured the mood perfectly.

This song has a spontaneous energetic sound. It opens with a series of power chords and builds up in intensity with a *crescendo* of feedback – one of the first times feedback had been used this way. 'My Generation' went on to become a classic of teenage rebellion – and has often been cited as a precursor of both hard rock and punk.

On the original studio recording of 'My Generation', Keith Moon played the shuffle groove which appears in this chart. Later live performances were considerably faster.

Aim to stress the ♩ beats and almost to 'ghost' the skip beat (the triplet ♪ which appears between the ♩ beats). This will help the rhythm retain its momentum. Be careful to avoid arm tension.

'*I hope* I die *before* I get *old*'

PRIMITIVE NOTION

New Order

When Ian Curtis, singer with the band Joy Division, committed suicide in 1980, the rest of the band agreed to continue under the name New Order, with the addition of the keyboard player Gillian Gilbert. They developed a different sound to that of Joy Division – one that was much more dance music and synthesiser-based.

New Order were very much part of the so-called 'Madchester' scene through the late 1980s and early 1990s – they were co-owners of the Hacienda nightclub and signed to Factory Records. 'Primitive Notion' is taken from the album *Get Ready* which was released in 2001 – their first release in eight years.

PERFORMANCE · HINTS & TIPS ·

There are ghosted notes woven into the texture throughout the 16-beat pattern of the verse. Ghost notes are soft, decorative sounds. They should be very light and provide a discreet additional layer to the groove. Be aware of the contrast between how high you lift your sticks when playing ghost notes and the height of your full strokes. The ghosted notes should contrast with the accented snare notes, which should be punchy and well projected.

In bars 45–48 you have an opportunity to make up your own solo. Stay within the style and feel of the song, but think about using syncopation, mixing strong beats with accented weaker beats, to create really exciting patterns.

'I want it to be like it did at the start'

WOULD?

Alice In Chains

Alice In Chains was an alternative metal band that was formed in Seattle during the late 1980s. Their outstanding bass player Mike Starr underpinned the other three members: Layne Staley (vocals), Jerry Cantrell (guitar, vocals) and Sean Kinney (drums). Alice In Chains are noted for their polished sound, unconventional vocal arrangements and heavy metal riffs which used amplified distortion to create a dark, dissonant sound.

'Would?' is from Alice In Chains' 1992 album *Dirt* – an angst-ridden work with many personal lyrics. It was a big hit after it featured in the film *Singles*.

PERFORMANCE · HINTS & TIPS ·

The dynamics in 'Would?' range from **mf** to **ff** . Make sure that the difference can be heard.

To play this song, you need secure independence between feet and hands. Important bass drum notes are very often on the weaker second and fourth ♪ in the bar and need to be very accurately placed. Aim to keep the patterns flowing. The big fill at bar 45 should be played as single strokes.

In the final bars you should silence the cymbal by 'choking' it with your hand.

'*Have* I run *too* far *to get* home?'

THE RAGGLE TAGGLE GYPSIES

Trad.

'The Raggle Taggle Gypsies' probably comes from Scotland – the first printed version dates from the early 18th century. The song came to be associated with the legendary love story of the gypsy Johnny Faa and Lady Jean Hamilton. In 1609, gypsies were expelled from Scotland and their love affair ended. Lady Jean married an earl but, years later, Johnny Faa returned and persuaded her to elope. The couple were caught; Johnny Faa and seven other gypsies were hanged and Lady Jean was imprisoned in a tower for the rest of her life.

There are many covers of this song, notably by The Waterboys, The Chieftains and Alison Moyet.

PERFORMANCE · HINTS & TIPS ·

The folk two-in-a-bar feel in this song has ghosted ♪ movement on snare with accents on the second and fourth ♩ of the bar. Ghost notes are soft, decorative sounds. In this passage, they should sit discreetly beneath the accents and provide a softer layer upon which the two and four can drive the groove onward. Be aware of the contrast between how high you lift your sticks when playing ghost notes and the height of your full strokes.

There are interesting fills at bars 39–40, 49–50 and 59–60. These are linear fills – the bass drum is used independently as part of the rhythmic line. Keep these bars flowing smoothly.

This song is also in the vocals, keyboards, guitar and bass books, so you can get together and play it in a band.

'How *could* you *leave* your *only* wedded *Lord?*'

AIRBAG

Radiohead

'Airbag' is taken from Radiohead's 1997 album *OK Computer*. The band, whose music is sometimes described as intelligent rock, is not afraid to experiment and takes influences not just from rock music, but also from contemporary classical, jazz, electronic and film music.

OK Computer is a complex album, with subtle rhythms, complex syncopations, and distorted guitars all helping to create unusual textures and atmospheres. In 'Airbag', Thom Yorke's plaintive voice delivers an oblique account of a near-fatal collision between a fast car and a juggernaut.

The drums do not play all the time in this song. They enter on the last beat of bar 5 and there are rests in bars 50–51, so you need to count. The entry in bar 5 starts with a drag on the snare drum which leads into a ♪ fill. Aim for a really effective drag to make the entry exciting.

There are fills throughout 'Airbag'. Judging what, how much and how loudly to play fills is one of the greatest challenges to any drummer. You should always think about the music that precedes and follows the fill – particularly the music that you are building towards. Some of the fills in 'Airbag' are marked 'light fills' – these are small transitional fills. Others are marked as 'big fills' and should be much more dramatic.

'Airbag' ends with three accented notes. Make these notes louder and place them carefully.

'I *am* back to save *the* universe'

WHITE ROOM

Cream

The band Cream comprised Eric Clapton (guitar), Jack Bruce (bass) and Ginger Baker (drums) – each of them highly accomplished rock musicians coming together as probably the first rock supergroup. Cream started as a blues revival band but their style gradually evolved into heavy rock. They were famous for their live performances and long improvised solos.

In 1968 Cream released their double album *Wheels Of Fire* – one of the albums was live and the other recorded in the studio. 'White Room' is the opening track of the studio album.

'White Room' opens in $\frac{5}{4}$ and then changes to $\frac{4}{4}$ at bar 9, returning to $\frac{5}{4}$ for the instrumental section.

The chorus is marked 'with a slight shuffle'. This means you should keep the ♪ notes straight, but the second and fourth ♪ notes can be played very slightly late – to imply a shuffle feel.

Be ready for the final cut-off, which is a ruff on the floor tom. It should be clearly articulated, landing firmly on the final note.

'*I'll* wait *in* this place where *the* sun *never* shines'

PLAYBACK

For your exam, you can choose either Playback or Improvising (see page 26).
If you choose Playback, you will be asked to play some music you have not seen or heard before.

In the exam, you will be given the song chart and the examiner will play a recording of the music. You will hear several two-bar or four-bar phrases on the recording: you should play each of them straight back in turn. There's a rhythm track going throughout, which helps you keep in time. There should not be any gaps in the music.

In the exam you will have two chances to play with the recording:
* First time – for practice
* Second time – for assessment.

You should listen to the audio, copying what you hear; you can also read the music. Here are some practice song charts which are also on the CD in this book. Don't forget that the Playback test can include requirements which may not be shown in these examples, including those from earlier grades. Check the parameters at www.trinityrock.com to prepare for everything which might come up in your exam.

Practice playback 1

TRACK 19

♩ = 76 (with a shuffle)

Practice playback 2

‘I really *like*
the *way*
music *looks* on *paper.*
It *looks* like *art*
to *me*’

Steve Vai

SESSION SKILLS

IMPROVISING

For your exam, you can choose either Playback (see page 24), or Improvising. If you choose to improvise, you will be asked to improvise over a backing track that you haven't heard before in a specified style.

In the exam, you will be given a song chart and the examiner will play a recording of the backing track. The backing track consists of a passage of music played on a loop. You should improvise a drum groove to it.

In the exam you will have two chances to play with the recording:
- First time – for practice
- Second time – for assessment.

Here are some improvising charts for practice which are also on the CD in this book. Don't forget that the Improvising test can include requirements which may not be shown in these examples, including those from earlier grades. Check the parameters at www.trinityrock.com to prepare for everything which might come up in your exam.

Practice improvisation 1

TRACK 21

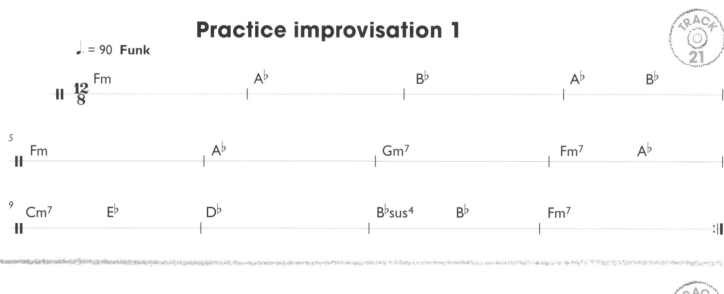

Practice improvisation 2

TRACK 22

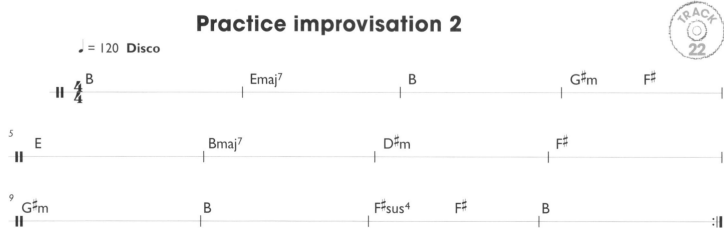

CHOOSING A SONG FOR YOUR EXAM

There are lots of options to help you choose your three songs for the exam.
For Songs 1 and 2, you can choose a song which is:

- from this book
- from www.trinityrock.com

Or for Song 2 you can choose a song which is:

- sheet music from a printed or online source
- your own arrangement of a song or a song you have written yourself (see page 28).

You can play the song unaccompanied or with a backing track (minus the drum part). If you like, you can create a backing track yourself (or with friends), or you could add your own vocals – or both.

For Grade 5, the song should last between two and three-and-a-half minutes, and the level of difficulty should be similar to your other songs. When choosing a song, think about:

- Does it work on my instrument?
- Are there any technical elements that are too difficult for me? (If so, perhaps save it for when you do the next grade.)
- Do I enjoy playing it?
- Does it work with my other pieces to create a good set-list?

See www.trinityrock.com for further information and advice on choosing your own song.

SHEET MUSIC

You must always bring an original copy of the book or a download sheet with email certificate for each song you perform in the exam. If you choose to write your own song you must provide the examiner with a copy of the sheet music. Your music can be:

- a lead sheet with lyrics, chords and melody line
- a chord chart with lyrics
- a full score using conventional staff notation
- see page 28 for details on presenting a song you have written yourself.

The title of the song and your name should be on the sheet music.

WRITING YOUR OWN SONG

You can play a song that you have written yourself for one of the choices in your exam. For Grade 5, your song should last between two and three-and-a-half minutes. It is sometimes difficult to know where to begin, however. Here are some suggestions for starting points:

- **A melody**: Many songs are made up around a hook (a short catchy melodic idea, usually only a few notes long). Try writing a couple of hooks:

- **Lyrics**: You could start by writing lyrics, or choosing someone else's lyrics (be aware of the copyright issues if you do this – see page 30 for further details). Your lyrics will help you decide whether your song will be upbeat or reflective, and may help you decide on a style and structure.

- **Structure**: Choose a structure for your song and write down a plan. For example, if you choose verse/chorus structure, your plan might be:

  verse: 12 bars, mainly E min and A min chords /
  chorus: 8 bars, G and D chords over two-bar bass riff /
  2 x verses: 2 x 12 bars /
  final chorus: 8 bars + 4-bar coda (G and D chords)

You might consider including bridge sections, solo passages, or a pre-chorus.
Or you might like to use an entirely different structure: 12-bar blues, AABA (where the first idea is repeated, then followed by a different section before repeating again at the end) . . .

There are plenty of other ways of starting: perhaps with a riff or a chord sequence, for example. You will also need to consider what **instruments** it is for (voice/keyboards/drums . . .).

There are many choices to be made – which is why writing a song is such a rewarding thing to do.

WRITING YOUR SONG DOWN

Rock and pop music is often written as a **lead sheet** with the lyrics (if there are any), chords and a melody line.

- As a drummer, you may want to write your part using **drum notation**, used for the songs in this book. There is a guide to this notation on page 31.

- You can, if you prefer, use a **graph** or **table** to represent your music, as long as it is clear to anyone else (including the examiner) how the song goes.

PLAYING IN A BAND

Playing in a band is exciting: it can be a lot of fun and, as with everything, the more you do it, the easier it gets. It is very different from playing on your own. Everyone contributes to the overall sound: the most important skill you need to develop is listening.

For a band to sound good, the players need to be 'together' – that mainly means keeping in time with each other, but also playing at the same volume, and with the same kind of feeling. Your relationship with the other band members is also important. Talk with them about the music you play, the music you like, and what you'd like the band to achieve short-term and long-term.

Band rehearsals are important – you should not be late, tired or distracted by your mobile phone! Being positive makes a huge difference. Try to create a friendly atmosphere in rehearsals so that everybody feels comfortable trying out new things. Don't worry about making mistakes: that is what rehearsals are for.

'The Raggle Taggle Gypsies' on page 10 is arranged for band. You will find parts for vocals, guitar, bass and keyboards in the other Trinity Rock & Pop Grade 5 books or available online. Trinity offers exams for groups of musicians at various levels. The songs arranged for bands are ideal to include as part of a set-list for these exams. Have a look at the website for more details.

HINTS AND TIPS

- Spend time planning your songs with the other band members. Think about who will play what, making the most of the instruments you have, and playing to the strengths of each band member. Be imaginative – the most exciting bands do not just copy what other bands have done, but play songs in new and unexpected ways.

- Record a demo. This can be a good way of giving the band a target to focus on. Make your demo the best you possibly can – record each song several times and discuss with the other band members which version works best. You can either record a demo in a studio, which enables you to edit your performances (combining the best bits of all your versions), or you can record your demo in 'live' conditions, which can give a more exciting demo but does not give you the opportunity to edit out any mistakes.

- Nothing beats the thrill of performing live in front of an audience. Organise a gig for a few friends. It can be a small gig in someone's house – the important thing is to get used to playing in front of other people. Gigs can be nerve-wracking at first, but try to relax and enjoy them.

PLAYING WITH BACKING TRACKS

The CD contains demos and backing tracks of all the songs in the book. The additional songs at www.trinityrock.com also come with demos and backing tracks.

- In your exam, you should perform with the backing track, or you can create your own (see below).
- The backing tracks begin with a click track, which sets the tempo and helps you start accurately.
- Be careful to set the balance between the volume of the backing track and your instrument.
- Listen carefully to the backing track to ensure you are playing in time.

If you are creating your own backing track here are some further tips:

- Make sure the sound quality is of a good standard.
- Think carefully about the instruments/sounds you are putting on the backing track.
- Avoid copying what you are playing on the backing track – it should support not duplicate.
- Do you need to include a click track at the beginning?

COPYRIGHT IN A SONG

If you are a singer or songwriter it is important to know about copyright. When someone writes a song or creates an arrangement they own the copyright (sometimes called 'the rights') to that version. The copyright means that other people cannot copy it, sell it, perform it in a concert, make it available online or record it without the owner's permission or the appropriate licence. When you write a song you automatically own the copyright to it, which means that other people cannot copy your work. But, just as importantly, you cannot copy other people's work, or perform it in public without their permission or the appropriate licence.

Points to remember

- You can create a cover version of a song and play it in an exam or other non-public performance.
- You cannot record your cover version and make your recording available to others (by copying it or uploading it to a website) without the appropriate licence.
- You do own the copyright of your own original song, which means that no one is allowed to copy it.
- You cannot copy someone else's song without their permission or the appropriate licence.

HELP PAGES

DRUM NOTATION GUIDE

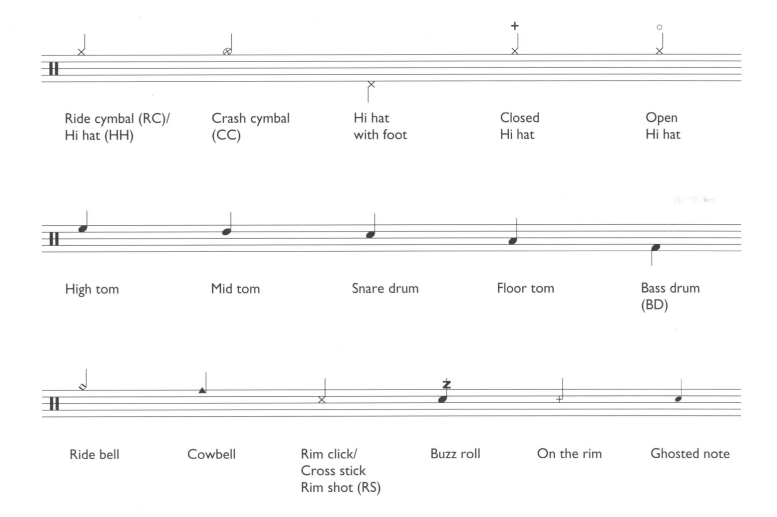

Ride cymbal (RC)/ Hi hat (HH)

Crash cymbal (CC)

Hi hat with foot

Closed Hi hat

Open Hi hat

High tom

Mid tom

Snare drum

Floor tom

Bass drum (BD)

Ride bell

Cowbell

Rim click/ Cross stick Rim shot (RS)

Buzz roll

On the rim

Ghosted note

ALSO AVAILABLE

Trinity College London Rock & Pop examinations 2012-2017 are also available for:

Bass Initial
ISBN: 978-0-85736-227-8

Bass Grade 1
ISBN: 978-0-85736-228-5

Bass Grade 2
ISBN: 978-0-85736-229-2

Bass Grade 3
ISBN: 978-0-85736-230-8

Bass Grade 4
ISBN: 978-0-85736-231-5

Bass Grade 5
ISBN: 978-0-85736-232-2

Bass Grade 6
ISBN: 978-0-85736-233-9

Bass Grade 7
ISBN: 978-0-85736-234-6

Bass Grade 8
ISBN: 978-0-85736-235-3

Drums Initial
ISBN: 978-0-85736-245-2

Drums Grade 1
ISBN: 978-0-85736-246-9

Drums Grade 2
ISBN: 978-0-85736-247-6

Drums Grade 3
ISBN: 978-0-85736-248-3

Drums Grade 4
ISBN: 978-0-85736-249-0

Drums Grade 5
ISBN: 978-0-85736-250-6

Drums Grade 6
ISBN: 978-0-85736-251-3

Drums Grade 7
ISBN: 978-0-85736-252-0

Drums Grade 8
ISBN: 978-0-85736-253-7

Guitar Initial
ISBN: 978-0-85736-218-6

Guitar Grade 1
ISBN: 978-0-85736-219-3

Guitar Grade 2
ISBN: 978-0-85736-220-9

Guitar Grade 3
ISBN: 978-0-85736-221-6

Guitar Grade 4
ISBN: 978-0-85736-222-3

Guitar Grade 5
ISBN: 978-0-85736-223-0

Guitar Grade 6
ISBN: 978-0-85736-224-7

Guitar Grade 7
ISBN: 978-0-85736-225-4

Guitar Grade 8
ISBN: 978-0-85736-226-1

Keyboards Initial
ISBN: 978-0-85736-236-0

Keyboards Grade 1
ISBN: 978-0-85736-237-7

Keyboards Grade 2
ISBN: 978-0-85736-238-4

Keyboards Grade 3
ISBN: 978-0-85736-239-1

Keyboards Grade 4
ISBN: 978-0-85736-240-7

Keyboards Grade 5
ISBN: 978-0-85736-241-4

Keyboards Grade 6
ISBN: 978-0-85736-242-1

Keyboards Grade 7
ISBN: 978-0-85736-243-8

Keyboards Grade 8
ISBN: 978-0-85736-244-5

Vocals Initial
ISBN: 978-0-85736-254-4

Vocals Grade 1
ISBN: 978-0-85736-255-1

Vocals Grade 2
ISBN: 978-0-85736-256-8

Vocals Grade 3
ISBN: 978-0-85736-257-5

Vocals Grade 4
ISBN: 978-0-85736-258-2

Vocals Grade 5
ISBN: 978-0-85736-259-9

Vocals Grade 6 (female voice)
ISBN: 978-0-85736-263-6

Vocals Grade 6 (male voice)
ISBN: 978-0-85736-260-5

Vocals Grade 7 (female voice)
ISBN: 978-0-85736-264-3

Vocals Grade 7 (male voice)
ISBN: 978-0-85736-261-2

Vocals Grade 8 (female voice)
ISBN: 978-0-85736-265-0

Vocals Grade 8 (male voice)
ISBN: 978-0-85736-262-9

HIGHLAND JOURNEY

Highland Journey

ROBIN GILLANDERS

Journey

In the Spirit of Edwin Muir

BIRLINN LTD | 2009

First published in 2009 by
Birlinn Limited
West Newington House
10 Newington Road
Edinburgh
EH9 1QS

www.birlinn.co.uk

ISBN: 978 1 84158 782 0

Extracts from Edwin Muir's *Scottish Journey* are reproduced
by permission of Mainstream Publishing, Edinburgh

British Library Cataloguing-in-Publication Data
A catalogue record for this book is available from the
British Library

Designed and typeset in Janson Text by James Hutcheson
Printed and bound in Slovenia

Contents

Preface

THE IDEA FOR THIS BOOK came some time after I found a copy of Michael Russell's *In Waiting* (1998) in Leakey's second-hand bookshop in Inverness in 2005. He had taken Edwin Muir's *Scottish Journey* as his model for a tour round Scotland prior to the (re-) establishment of a Scottish Parliament in 1999.

Reading his account, and subsequently Muir's *Journey*, it gradually dawned on me that a photographic journey, in the spirit of Edwin Muir's, would be an interesting undertaking. It has occurred to me that sometimes travel writing lacks good photography to accompany it; and conversely, that photographic documentary would benefit from a narrative element – or at least extended captions – to complement it. But any accompanying text should preferably be written by the photographer to avoid the possibility that an image might be misinterpreted or misrepresented by a separate commentator. Frequently I have been seduced by the imagery of classic documentary photography yet also frustrated that I could not learn more about particular subjects. It is still a great misconception that the documentary photograph should be able to stand alone.

In attempting to combine words and images, I am painfully aware that my skills as a photographer are certainly superior to my writing skills; reading and re-reading Muir it seemed an impertinence even to attempt to match his eloquent prose. Consequently, what follows should be regarded as photographs accompanied by words rather than the converse. My text has been necessarily brief and personal; I hope I shall be forgiven for dipping superficially into complex historical and contemporary issues which deserve a more scholarly appraisal than I have been able to provide.

In the realisation of this project, I am indebted first of all to Michael Russell, not just for the initial idea inspired by his book *In Waiting*, but for his subsequent enthusiastic encouragement and support.

Constructed portraits are always a collaboration between photographer and sitter, and I am extremely grateful to all those who patiently and graciously submitted to be photographed. I am similarly grateful to the many people with whom I spoke on the journey, and who provided me with valuable insights. In particular I would like to thank John Charity, Dominic Cooper, Dr Finlay MacLeod and Jean Urquhart. And in Orkney, Alistair Peebles, Andrew Parkinson and Neil Firth at the Pier Arts Centre, Bryce Wilson, and Liza and Brian Murray.

My long-suffering friend, the photographer Chris Hall, provided me with initial advice on the purchase of a suitable campervan, generously lent me items of photographic equipment and readily agreed to a first reading of the manuscript.

I am also grateful to Julie Lawson of the Scottish National Portrait Gallery and Cathy Shankland of Highland Council, who first exhibited the work in Scotland House in Brussels and then in Highland Council galleries.

This project has been an expensive undertaking, and could not have been accomplished without the initial support of the Scottish Arts Council and Hi-Arts. I am also grateful to Napier University for allowing me some respite from teaching in order to undertake the latter stages of the 'journey'. In addition I would like to acknowledge the generous contribution of the Scottish Government and Highland Council for financing the production of the initial exhibitions.

Finally, grateful thanks to my wife, Marjory – as ever. Her never-ending support kept my morale buoyant throughout the whole project, from initial concept to final realisation.

Robin Gillanders
December 2008

Introduction

In June of 1934 the writer and poet Edwin Muir borrowed a car from his friend, fellow Orcadian and contemporary, Stanley Cursiter, then the director of the National Galleries of Scotland, and set out on a tour around Scotland. In his book *Scottish Journey*, published the following year, he states, '. . . my intention in beginning it was to give my impressions of contemporary Scotland; not the romantic Scotland of the past nor the Scotland of the tourist, but the Scotland which presents itself to one who is not looking for anything in particular, and is willing to believe what his eyes and his ears tell him'.

Several writers have made journeys throughout Scotland: Boswell and Johnson in the eighteenth century, Robert Louis Stevenson in the nineteenth, and Muir, James Campbell and Michael Russell in the twentieth. The last two both tip a hat to Muir. It could be argued that, historically, Muir is the most interesting: he writes before the cataclysmic social, economic and political change brought about by World War Two and yet much of his narrative has strong resonances with today. He worries at the nature of Scottish identity, and its erosion by (in those days, English) incomers, and he comments on tourism and depopulation.

During the early months of 2006 I began to plan an extended journey around the Scottish Highlands and Orkney inspired by Muir's travels – not as a writer, but as a photographer. It's difficult to estimate, but Muir's journey round the whole of Scotland probably lasted two to three weeks, including six days spent travelling through the Highlands on his way to Orkney. I knew that my journey would take a great deal longer. It seems paradoxical, but photography is a slower process than writing. The writer records his thoughts and impressions, sometimes long after the experience as Muir did, whereas the photographer has to photograph what is there. You can't photograph a thought. Subjects have to be contacted and arrangements made; research *in situ* has to be carried out and due attention has to be paid to The Light. There's a great deal of enforced inactivity involved in photography.

The section of Muir's *Journey* that covered the Highlands amounts to approximately a quarter of the book and is full of fascinating and eloquent anecdotes and descriptions. There is, however, very little reference to the political, social and economic issues facing the Highlands and Orkney at that time, save for some subjective opinion. As a romantic socialist and quasi-nationalist, it's clear that he had knowledge of these issues, but he doesn't directly deal with them. Again and again, Muir refers to 'impressions'; he is not attempting an academic socio-political study but rather a personal response: 'a thin layer of objectivity super-imposed on a large mass of memory'. I wished to divert, not just from Muir's route, but from his remit, by commenting on some of the major contemporary issues facing these remote areas.

As an Orcadian, Muir considered himself to be both an insider and an outsider from Scotland; as a Lowlander, I have a similar relationship with the Highlands, which even today is radically different, socially and economically, to my home town of Edinburgh. Naturally, I had made many previous visits to the Highlands, so I cannot say that I was without preconceptions, however, I have tried to be true to Muir's principle in that I would respond to what I saw. This then, was to be a highly partial account of one person's impressions of the Highlands.

I was aware that I was attempting a project that was very traditional – and unfashionable – in concept. I wanted to work with a 5 × 4 inch camera and black-and-white film to produce highly formal and constructed pictures. I intended following the example, not just of Muir, but of classic documentary photographers like Paul Strand, who spent three months in South Uist in 1954. The resulting pictures, published as *Tir A'Mhurain* are not only fine examples of photographic art, but an important historical record of a community experiencing protracted and radical change. It did occur to me that I was (ambitiously and arrogantly) attempting to do for the whole of the Highlands and Orkney what Strand did for tiny South Uist, in the same timeframe.

I purchased a 30-year-old large-format folding camera and various lenses on an internet auction site and finally located a second-hand campervan small enough to easily navigate Highland roads, but which could accommodate a darkroom. The shower compartment was converted for this purpose and a scanner installed, so that I could process sheets of film, scan them and view them 'on the road' on a laptop computer. Further embracing the digital age, I took with me a compact digital camera to use as a visual notebook.

In the event, I spent a total of 80 days in the van between the beginning of June and the end of October 2006, and made some 75 final pictures from about 250 exposures, from which I have selected 50. I covered some 5,000 miles, but not as a continuous journey as I had hoped and imagined, since various personal demands meant that I had to break my journey on occasions. A journal was kept throughout, from which the following text has been gleaned and embellished.

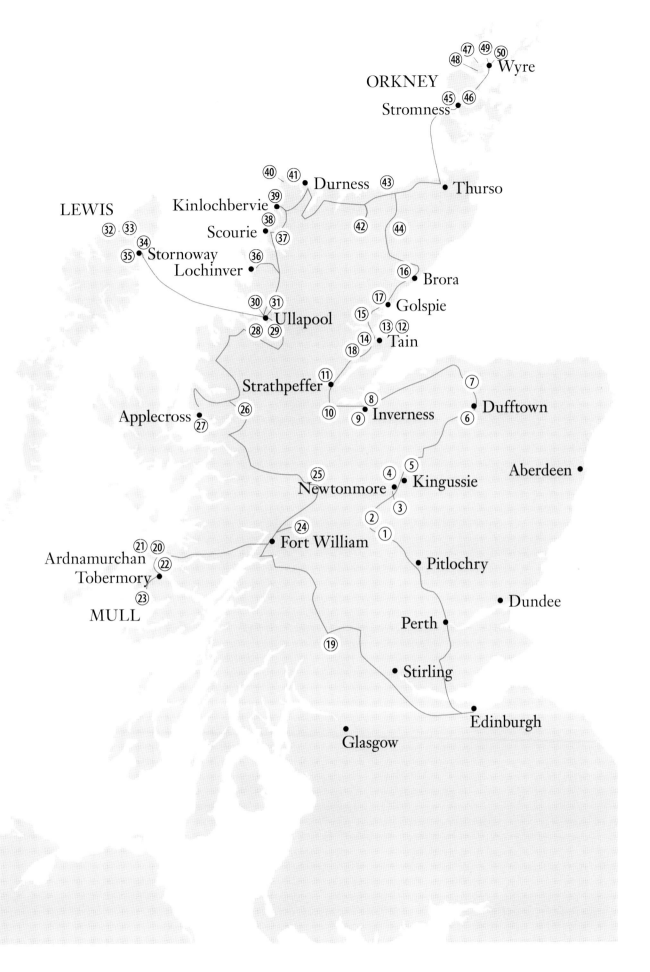

ORKNEY

Wyre
㊼ ㊾ ㊿
㊽
㊺ ㊻
Stromness

Thurso

⑳ ㊶ Durness ㊸
Kinlochbervie ㊴
Scourie ㊳ ㊲
LEWIS
㉜ ㉝
㉞ ㊷ ㊶
㉟ Stornoway
Lochinver ㊱

Brora
⑯
⑰ Golspie
⑮
⑬ ⑫
㉚ ㉛
Ullapool ⑭ Tain
㉘ ㉙ ⑱

⑪
Strathpeffer ⑦
㉖ ⑧
Applecross ⑩ Inverness Dufftown
㉗ ⑨ ⑥

⑤
④ ⑤
㉕
Newtonmore Kingussie
Aberdeen
③

②

㉔
⑳ ⑳ ①
Ardnamurchan ㉑ ㉒ Fort William
Tobermory Pitlochry

㉓
MULL
Dundee

Perth

⑲

Stirling

Edinburgh

Glasgow

I I

Pass of Drumochter

I left Edinburgh in early June – later than I had intended since the demands of work and getting the van ready had delayed my departure. Drizzle and drabness did nothing to dampen my excitement: it reminded me of my first short escapes northwards after I learnt to drive in my early twenties. But given my advancing years and the growing timidity that seems to be their natural correlation, I was also quite nervous. Nervous about how I, a city boy, would cope with extended periods of solitude and the logistics of campervanning, but particularly nervous about whether I could produce anything worthwhile. It seemed such a massive project.

I took the Great North Road, as it used to be called. Now, less romantically, it's just the A9. This was the route that Muir took – unsurprising because it's the main arterial route north. It's a lot faster now than it was then. Even when I first travelled it in the 1970s it was a slow road. Now the new road has stretches of dual carriageway; it also has much more traffic and long bends where, dangerously, you are not sure whether you can overtake or not. Each section bears witness to its own tragedies.

Muir wrote that the Highlands proper begin a little way north of Dunkeld – I always reckoned it was Drumochter. The sign on the A9 at the Pass of Drumochter says 'Welcome to the Highlands', so it must be true. And as I passed it the sun suddenly emerged in that way so typical of and unique to northern Scotland. A welcome indeed. This is the gateway to the Highlands and it carries the essentials of communication so vital to a modernised Scotland north of Perth. The Pass is the highest point on any railway in Britain.

I stopped briefly at Drumochter Lodge, where I used to go grouse-beating as a teenager. Ironically it's the Game Conservancy Trust now. I didn't quite have the nerve to introduce myself.

I drove on to Newtonmore and on the outskirts, rounding a bend, I suddenly saw a hand-painted sign for a campsite (this wasn't mentioned in the guides to campsites that I'd read!). Great – I called at the house and booked in with a stern-looking Highland woman (from Inverness, she said). A friendly discussion ensued about Highland accents, whether Invernesians really do speak the purest English (no they don't, she said), and about incomers telling them how to run their affairs. Five pounds a night; no electrical hook-up. I parked, extricated the bike from the back of the van and cycled into Newtonmore.

2

Highland landscape, Dalwhinnie

My first night in the van and I woke at the campsite in Newtonmore to a fresh and intermittently sunny morning and with nothing planned. Feeling that I needed to be active, I headed off to explore the region and backtracked to Dalwhinnie.

I began to enjoy driving this van with its homely chug-chug diesel engine, having spent most of my life rushing. It's difficult to rush in a van, and you wouldn't want to anyway in the Highlands. And it's nice to be high up so you can see over hedges and dykes. There is, apparently, a convention that one waves to passing campervanners if they are British, much in the same way that Reliant Robin owners used to when they passed each other. I reluctantly adopted this practice. After a while it became quite nice to exchange a greeting, however insincere, when travelling alone. I drew the line at motorhomes though. Ironically, however, I began to notice that, with pleasant but rare exceptions, fellow travellers are not too friendly in campsites. Mainly they are 'older' couples or young families and probably think that the solitary male is a bit odd.

One gains the impression that the melancholic Muir was content in his solitary journey: he was a shy observer rather than a participator, and during his frequent hotel stops he preferred his own company and taking solitary walks to enduring his fellow guests in the lounge. I like to think that if campervans had been invented then, he would have wished to make his journey in one.

Passing into the Highlands, Muir describes his impressions of this 'wild and solitary scenery' and 'the added value which every natural object acquires from one's consciousness, that it has not been touched by the human will. The larch woods, the streams, all of them noisy and active . . . the little mounds of turf: all had an exhilarating freshness which is absent from more cultivated places, and seemed to exist completely in themselves, as if they were their own end.'

The Highlands are really the only place in the UK where there is extensive opportunity to be alone, and I found as my journey progressed that I preferred 'wild camping' to the convenience of campsites. Really, such natural and awesome beauty is best experienced alone. The corollary of widespread improved communications and easier access, with all the attendant economic benefits, is that summer brings more and more visitors who strike further and further north, threatening culture, environment . . . and solitude.

3

Rob Ritchie, former shinty chieftain, Newtonmore

As I walked to the pub in Newtonmore that evening, I passed a kid apparently wearing full football kit but carrying a shinty stick. I would have loved to ask him if I could make a portrait, but I'm shy and in any case asking kids if you can photograph them is definitely dodgy these days. I realised that if I was to make anything of this photographic journey, I had to overcome my shyness.

I was warmed by the idea that, despite the attraction of television and computer games, here was a kid who had embraced that traditional and almost exclusively Highland sport. Thank goodness he wasn't clutching a baseball bat. It's encouraging that there are some activities that are particularly Highland, for a Highland populace, and not just aimed at tourists.

The next day I crossed the road from the campsite and visited the shinty ground, where I met who I thought was the groundsman working on the pitch. Rob Ritchie is a former chieftain of the Newtonmore Camanachd Club, which is one of the most famous shinty clubs in Scotland and has a traditional rivalry with neighbouring Kingussie. We had a long chat and he told me in a quiet and gentle Highland accent about the game and the changes made over the years – most of which he disapproves of. In particular the change from winter to summer shinty has meant that the game has suffered from competition with the summer sports of golf, bowls and Highland games as well as other summer activities. On the other hand, the move to the summer has meant that it avoids a clash with the more popular town games of rugby and football in the winter, and that it might attract a tourist audience. It seemed to me that it would be tragic if one of the last great amateur games should continue to experience financial problems and see sponsorship decline. For a long time the game has suffered from its geographical remoteness in that young players often move away to cities for study and employment, so there is less team continuity than in urban sports. And yet it seems an important focus for an indigenous community continuing to decline.

That afternoon I processed my first batch of film in the van, managing to ruin a couple due to inept loading of the developing tank. More practice required . . .

4

Gentlemen's Hairdresser, Newtonmore

Is it possible in this part of the Highlands to escape from an economy that seems weighted towards tourism and leisure? The drive around the minor roads from Ruthven in a circular route to Kingussie and Newtonmore was idyllic – but the charm is tinged with a feeling of discomfort that so many of the houses are clearly newly built – or extensively renovated – and very expensive. Probably they are holiday homes, financially totally out of reach of the majority of local people. English and southern accents abound and most of the Highlanders left here seem to be elderly – with the exception of Rob Ritchie and the woman who runs the campsite. Most young people move to the cities.

I needed some black Velcro to improve the blackout in my tiny mobile darkroom and enquired at several shops in Kingussie and Newtonmore. I didn't hear one Scottish accent. Shops and small businesses servicing a local community seem to have gradually given way to cafés and craft shops aimed at a tourist market. Most of them probably close in winter and I was to discover that a similar story is to be told all over the Highlands. The burgeoning 'heritage industry' is seen as important for tourism and the Newtonmore area has an abundance of attractions, including the excellent Highland Folk Museum.

All this was in my mind when I planned this picture. I had calculated that the sun would be in the right position at around 3 p.m., which gave me plenty of time to investigate the Clan Macpherson Museum, just across the road.

That evening, feeling I had made a successful photograph, I rewarded myself with an excellent curry served by a friendly Polish girl in a hotel run by an Englishman and packed with tourists.

I returned to Newtonmore a year later to discover that the building had been demolished. I also learned that the signage had been erected by a film crew for the television series *Monarch of the Glen*, an inoffensive, light-hearted but ersatz depiction of Highland life. Local hoteliers and tourist offices had been quick to make capital out of the popular series and seemed happy to acquiesce in this romanticised portrayal of Highland life. Apparently the building at various times had been a chemist's and a baker's (both serving a local population) – but Newtonmore had never had a 'Gentlemen's Hairdressers', at least not that anyone could remember. Never trust a photograph.

5

Ruthven Barracks, Kingussie

By the end of my first week, I had begun to establish a routine of retiring to bed early and waking early – usually prompted by demands of the bladder. Since I was reluctant to use the chemical toilet in the van, which in any case was in my cluttered darkroom, this meant dressing and visiting the toilet block (if I was in a campsite), after which I was usually reluctant to get back into bed. Such are the necessary privations in the service of Art.

So it was that I woke early, to bright sunshine, with the intention of driving the few miles to Ruthven Barracks just outside Kingussie. Any photographer will say that the best time to photograph landscape is early in the morning, or in the evening when the sun is low in the sky.

While it was never my intention (or Muir's) to provide a tourist travelogue, I felt that some references to history were appropriate. After all, a nation's identity is defined in part by its history and it's difficult to escape that in the Highlands. The Scots, home and abroad, seem to have a nostalgic and sometimes morbid obsession with the past, nourished since Scott wrote his *Waverley* novels by literature, film and the heritage industry.

This barracks was one of a series of four built by the government after the 1715 rebellion to keep the clans in check. It was captured by the Jacobites in February of 1746 and then burnt down by them three months later, just after their disastrous defeat at Culloden.

The failure of the '45 rebellion triggered brutal government retaliation, marking the beginning of the erosion of Highland culture and leading ultimately to the Clearances and depopulation. It's all tragically romantic and sentimental stuff. It has led Scots from all over the country – and abroad – to identify with the separate and specific historical misfortunes of the Highlands. We often choose to ignore the fact that Lowland Scots, some Highland clans and Highland landlords, were often as complicit in this attrition as the English. And the irony is that, ever since the late eighteenth century, in the eyes of the monarchy and in particular George IV, tartan and bagpipes came to be identified with Scotland as a whole while the real Highland culture was being relentlessly eroded by Clearances. The Highlanders, who hitherto were seen as thieves, gradually came to represent the whole of Scotland.

6

Pearl McKenna, The Royal Oak, Dufftown

Time to move on, aware that my output of photographs needed to be faster if I was to produce a significant body of work within the timescale. Muir spent six days travelling through the Highlands on his way to Orkney and I always knew it would take me a lot longer, but I now realised that I could not rely on 'serendipity' as Muir did; I would need to plan my pictures better, decide who and what I would photograph and what issues I would comment on.

I was glad to be away from Newtonmore, though, and diverting from Muir's route up the A9, decided to investigate Speyside. I booked into a rather posh (and expensive) campsite at Aberlour. It had good facilities and an electrical hook-up so that I could run my laptop and my scanner (which I used for scanning negatives) as long as I liked.

There is a real feeling that Aberlour and neighbouring Dufftown are working towns. They have a purpose: mainly Walker's Shortbread and whisky. Dufftown is the self-styled malt whisky capital of Scotland, and most of the dozens of distilleries in the area also have visitor centres for tourists. Ironically, they probably employ more people than the distilleries themselves. On Saturday night there were a lot of young people out on the street – perhaps the typical disaffected youth that is to be found in most small towns. There are two chip shops and two wee supermarkets – surely an index of a working population and not just passing or hotel-staying tourists. It seemed so different from Newtonmore and Kingussie.

The Royal Oak was typical of many Scottish bars in rural areas – no frills and no sign of tourists. The regulars crowd the bar in the evenings as if they are part of the furniture, and eye strangers with passing interest but not hostility. Drinking and the sociability of bars is an important part of rural community life – at least for the male population.

Pearl is originally from Glasgow and has an easy and relaxed friendliness – not put on, showy, or disingenuous – like the bar itself. She has the gift that so many Glaswegians appear to have, of being able to chat away as if she'd known me for years. Her wee dog Nipper scampered around, occasionally leaping onto the bar to greet a favoured punter.

John Richard, cooper, Speyside Cooperage, Craigellachie

Whisky is such an important part of the Scottish economy – and culture – that I felt that it demanded another picture. It's one of the major export industries of the Highlands and a principal employer in Speyside. I had passed the 'Speyside Cooperage' with its colossal pyramids of casks on my way to Dufftown from the campsite, and had wondered if I might be able to make a picture here. So I asked Pearl at the Royal Oak if she knew any coopers and she said that Rachel, her barmaid at the Royal Oak, was engaged to one and that he had just finished his four-year apprenticeship. Indeed, he had been in the traditional barrel of tar only the previous week. Rachel agreed to text him, and he agreed to be photographed, subject to his boss's approval.

I spent most of the next day looking round the vast area of the cooperage, trying to decide how I would photograph him. The cooperage is the only one left in the Highlands that is independent and family run. It came as a surprise to me that the coopers are on piece work, so that they are only paid for what they produce. This seems somewhat Victorian, but the coopers are apparently happy with it. It did mean, though, that in the time spent making the portrait, John would be losing money, and I wondered how much it would cost him to go to the toilet. There is a visitor centre where you can look down voyeuristically on the workers' focused and hectic activity from behind a Perspex screen. Having made a decision on the portrait, I made six exposures in fifteen minutes and allowed him to escape back to his casks.

We arranged to meet in the Royal Oak that evening. Quietly self-effacing, John told me over a pint about his plans for the future now that he had finished his apprenticeship. He said that he and Rachel planned to be married the following April and had seen an inexpensive three-bedroom flat with garden for £65,000. They are both from Dufftown and wanted to stay on – unlike so many young people in the Highlands – but then there is a variety of employment in the area. He revealed that he had applied for a mortgage, to be told that it may be a problem because he has no credit rating. John had never been in debt in his life – even his mobile phone was pay-as-you-go. It seems that before you can borrow money, even if you have stable employment, you need to have been in debt.

8

Inverness Industrial Estate

I left Aberlour for Inverness at 9.30 a.m. amid glorious crisp sunshine, rejoining Muir's route at Carrbridge. Even though I have visited Inverness on several occasions, it still came as something of a shock to drive through some of the wildest and most beautiful scenery in Europe and then come over a hill and encounter an urban sprawl. Arriving at about 1 p.m., I found a campsite on the outskirts that was more like a prison camp than a holiday park, with high fences and a gate that, we were sternly warned, would be shut at 11 p.m. The taciturn Scot who was in charge was not at all friendly as he directed me to a pitch very near to his office. Great that it was near the toilets, but I realised that he wanted me close by so that he could keep an eye on me, as a suspicious-looking lone camper. Unfairly perhaps, it was to colour my whole impression of Inverness on that visit. Muir obviously didn't like Inverness much either: 'Inverness gave me the impression I have always had on visiting it; that is, of being inconveniently crowded with vehicles of all kinds, most of them stationary.'

Inverness has been expanding. Having been granted city status in 2001, it is now, apparently, the fastest growing city in Western Europe. There has been an ongoing process, particularly since the re-establishment of the Scottish Parliament in 1999, of consciously changing the political centre of gravity away from the Central Belt and relocating some government agencies here, like Scottish Natural Heritage. I bet the staff weren't happy.

Rapid expansion has brought about change in the Invernesian way of life. While the traditional industries have seriously declined, they have been replaced by high-tech industries and retail. Ghastly and geographically inappropriate retail parks have been built in recent years. Needless to say, most of the expansion of the city has been as a result of incomers from the south and also significantly from Eastern Europe, who have a reputation for being very hard-working and are increasingly vital for the service industries. But Inverness is just as rapidly losing its Highland identity.

Too-rapid expansion has brought with it some of the social problems associated with the larger towns and cities of the Central Belt. The traditional Highland relationship with alcohol has been supplemented by a growing drugs problem – along with that comes homelessness, and what we think of as the associated urban problems of depression and suicide.

9

Kim Gordon, Inverness pedestrian precinct

Wandering around the centre of Inverness, it was clear that real attempts have been made to 'improve' the urban environment, but these shopping malls and pedestrian precincts still seem dismal. Sitting on a bench in the High Street sharing warm sunshine with crowds of Saturday shoppers, there was the strong feeling that I could have been in any town in Britain with similar architecture and chain stores. Everywhere there was the same globalised uniform of denim, tee shirts and trainers. If there is a Highland identity, it is not to be found here in the architecture or the way people dress.

The only individual I could see who didn't conform to the blueprint was a stallholder selling ethnic jewellery near to a display of morose-looking birds of prey tethered to short perches. He agreed to a portrait, but the harsh sunlight was a problem and we agreed to meet later. While I was self-consciously setting up the camera, a youngish man came over and asked if I was a professional photographer. He was a keen amateur and it seems he had been a fish farmer in Shieldaig on the west coast. I asked him about the percentage of Scots in Inverness and he said that three years previously there would have been mainly Scots but recently there has been an influx of about 2,500 Polish people. It does seem increasingly multicultural. After I made Kim's portrait, I promised to send him a print and he gave his address as: Kim's Stall, c/o High Street, Beside TSB Bank.

Subsequently I discovered that Kim has been a permanent fixture in the High Street for 20 years. He sounded as if he might be a Londoner and one can only speculate about why he should have left to come as far as Inverness. He had lived in a caravan for some years before building a house on the outskirts. Apparently he has raised an immense amount for charity through activities such as annual swims across Loch Ness. Cities need eccentrics.

That afternoon, hoping for a more congenial campsite, I decided to head for Beauly. Muir decided to move on there after taking afternoon tea in Inverness, because he 'wanted to stay in a smaller town than Inverness'. I had to agree with him.

10

Caledonian Hotel, Beauly

I found a pleasantly wooded and secluded campsite just outside Beauly with the usual facilities: electrical hook-up and plenty of fresh water taps. The pitches were well spaced out and randomly scattered rather than being regimented. I had begun to tune in to these places – some felt good and others didn't and it's difficult to say precisely why that was. Perhaps it's something to do with the classical notion of spirit of place, or more prosaically just my state of mind at the time. Having established my pitch, I drove into Beauly. It's an agreeable, well-heeled small town with an unusually wide street, the centre of which is choked with parked cars. Muir commented on it as '. . . resembling more than anything else a continental market square set down in the country, with a few low houses to define with studied carelessness its outline'.

Wandering around in warm, late afternoon sunshine, I speculated in a dreamy sort of way about which of the hotels Muir might have stayed in. I like to think that he stayed at the Caledonian – agreeably shabby-looking and seemingly about the right vintage. Certainly he described looking out on the main street from his bedroom window. The bar was closed for refurbishment and I fervently hoped it would not be turned into a bistro or (hell mend us), an 'eaterie' or that they would change the hotel name. I wondered how many Caledonian Hotels there are in Scotland, and how many have lost their names in favour of something more contemporary. Terrible crimes have been perpetrated in the name of renovation and 'improvement'.

I bought some sausages for my dinner at the Spar store and ate a bag of chips from the takeaway as an hors d'oeuvre. Back at the campsite, relieved to be alone, I opened a bottle of wine and, as had become customary, plugged in my laptop and wrote an entry in my journal before frying my tea.

11

Strathpeffer

The next morning I drove a few mile west to Ffordes, which is a massive online photographic store that used to be in the south of England but is now located quite near to Beauly. I needed a replacement flash cable and I also wanted a cheap rucksacktype camera bag for the 5 × 4 kit. I was pleased to find that an ex-student of mine was working there and he sold me a second-hand bag at a good price. Then, retracing my route, I headed north from Beauly and made a conscious decision to divert from Muir's route at Contin. Instead of heading west towards Ullapool as he did, I diverted to the east driving through benign and pastoral farmland and pleasant small villages. In a short time I found myself in Strathpeffer. If Inverness seems to sit uneasily within its surrounding countryside, so in a different way does Strathpeffer. It's an incongruous architectural curiosity which seemed totally at odds with the surrounding Highland countryside.

Strathpeffer developed along with the burgeoning tourism industry in the nineteenth century following Queen Victoria's long-standing love affair with the Highlands. This and romantic notions of Highland culture and history, promoted principally through the novels of Sir Walter Scott, put the Highlands very much on the map as a tourist destination. The coming of the railway greatly facilitated this, arriving in Dingwall in the 1860s and then in Strathpeffer in the 1880s, bringing wealthy Victorian visitors from as far as the south of England to this spa town. The railway station closed in 1951 but the town continues to be a tourist destination hosting busloads of them in huge hotels.

After making a picture of a particularly grand, privately owned Victorian mansion, I sat on the steps outside the Pavilion and watched an enormous coach from Yorkshire disgorge dozens of elderly sightseers. I didn't stop long in Strathpeffer and headed on up the east coast.

12

Fishing net drying poles, Portmahomack

Continuing up the east coast on the A9, traffic was heavy, the weather flat, and the landscape unremarkable. I had thought that I would head straight for Tain, which I knew from a few previous visits, but driving on up the Cromarty Firth, I began to think about an old school friend who used to holiday in Portmahomack, which is a diversion east on to a peninsula. I had always wondered what it was like but had never the time nor the motivation to visit. I had read James Campbell's *Invisible Country* (1984), and he had visited Portmahomack and mentioned a campsite which 'forbade the entrance or exit of vehicles on a Sunday'. Although it was marked on the OS map, it wasn't listed on my map of Scottish campsites. Nevertheless, I took the diversion right just south of Tain.

Meandering through rich, rolling fields of corn, I found the site on the edge of the village beside the Tarbet Free Church. A sign on the gate did indeed tell me that movement of traffic was forbidden on a Sunday and that enquiries were to be made at the manse. Nothing changed then, in at least 20 years. A young lad (the minister's son?), quiet and slightly guarded, booked me in and gave me a key to the toilets. It's a lovely site right on the beach with adequate facilities but no hook-up. I was pleased that it wasn't well advertised.

Keen to make a picture, I heaved the camera and tripod onto to my back and cycled into 'the Port'. It's a picturesque wee place with some smart, rather self-satisfied, whitewashed houses along the front. There are dozens of similar fishing villages down the east coast of Scotland where now not much fishing goes on. Portmahomack is a tourist destination these days, with a golf course, small marina, a Carnegie Hall and a Caledonian Hotel.

The herring and whitefish industries were a major employer on the east coast throughout the nineteenth century, reaching their peak before World War One and falling into steady decline afterwards. This was for a variety of reasons, including a decrease in demand from Germany and Russia, and later because of over-fishing. Now there is some inshore fishing for prawns (sold as langoustines!) and lobsters, but mainly fishing is for leisure, and since the oil-platform construction yard opened at nearby Nigg in 1972 most fishermen left their nets to work there.

A century ago the population would double during the season with hundreds of boats and attendant herring curers coming in. Now it probably doubles in the summer with tourists, holiday-homers – and campers.

Rev. John MacLeod, Portmahomack

The following day I slept later than usual, to be woken by the apocalyptic scream and thunderous rumble of low-flying Tornado jets which use a coastal area a few miles due east as a bombing range. I packed the bed away, made coffee and decided to head into Tain to buy a paper and some badly needed food supplies. The previous evening I had thought about the Free Church and the boy from the manse who had booked me into the site, and I decided then that I would attempt a portrait of the minister. I was pleased that I had a plan, and rather than drop in on him, I phoned him from Tain. A friendly voice readily agreed to meet that afternoon.

The cheerful figure of John MacLeod greeted me at the door to the manse with his daughter Flora and his son Malcolm, who has Down's syndrome. Another son, Peter (the campsite warden), remained upstairs. We sat round his kitchen table, where I was served coffee and biscuits by Flora and Malcolm while John had some sort of herbal tea. As I reached for a biscuit, I realised that the others were saying grace.

It is hardly appropriate here to provide a history of the Free Church of Scotland since the 1843 Disruption, or to provide a critical overview of its fundamental beliefs and its continuing disciplinarian influence in parts of the Highlands, especially Lewis and Harris. Suffice it to say that its hold over remote communities has steadily diminished over the last few decades for the same reasons that other aspects of the Highland way of life have been eroded.

Throughout its existence the Free Church has been beset by continual splits (and reunions), with most congregations having rejoined the Established Church in 1921. John spoke at length and with a mixture of sadness and relish about the most recent schism of the Free Church in 2000, in which he was closely involved.

While his children sat silently and patiently in attendance, he told me about a sexual scandal involving a case against a Free Church theological professor which began in the Church courts and ended in the Court of Session. When the case was thrown out, John and 22 other ministers protested, and this led to the 'main' Free Church attempting to have them removed from office, including not being allowed to preach as ministers. They constituted the Free Church (Continuing), and there then proceeded seriously acrimonious disputes over Church assets and property. It was fascinating stuff and he was a good storyteller with a strong academic knowledge of Church history and much else. It all made the bear-pit of politics seem like a nursery. Since the split, John said that his congregation has reduced from about 50 to around 30.

14

Liz White, The Railway Hotel, Tain

The following day, I reluctantly decided to leave Portmahomack and to move to the campsite just outside Tain. While I would have liked to stay another night, it was Saturday and if I stayed on I would have had to remain there until Monday. So after stopping briefly in Tain, I booked into a very neat and friendly site with excellent facilities, and spent most of the day processing films and scanning negatives.

I had been to the Railway Hotel on previous occasions and for some time had wondered whether I might make a picture of the manager. So, late in the afternoon, I drove into town and had a drink in the bar – and it was she who served me. The bar was quiet and we chatted about Tain and how she came to be there. Summoning up courage, I eventually asked if I could do a portrait and, after studying me for a few seconds with the merest hint of suspicion, to my surprise she agreed with a smile and we organised a time for later on that evening.

Tain seems a genteel and attractive town. The only evidence to the contrary is that there are signs posted on lampposts all round the High Street warning that there are fines for drinking on the streets. And on the entrances to bars names are posted of those who are barred, and for how long. The town has attempted to deal with youth-drinking problems, but karaoke and discos have arrived here. Liz's bar runs a disco on a Friday and Saturday and has three bouncers on the door. On these nights, when tourists are safely in hotel bars and restaurants, Tain seems like the Wild West.

Liz moved to Tain about 25 years ago when her husband came to work at Nigg. She said that a lot of Glaswegians came up to work there; houses were built for them in Alness and when the work dried up some stayed on. But not her husband – he left and she stayed. She had wanted to retire but agreed to manage the hotel. As a Glaswegian, she is very like Pearl in Dufftown: the same undemonstrative friendliness and at the same time, a feeling that hers has not been an easy life.

I find all portraits stressful, but this was particularly so, despite Liz's good humour and patience. It was made at about 9 p.m., with bar staff Alan and Willie. Six exposures were made quickly, with kids swarming about and the light fading.

15

Aly Bain and Phil Cunningham, Carnegie Hall, Clashmore

I had planned to make a portrait of my friends Aly and Phil at some point during the journey and I knew that, coincidentally, they were playing the village hall in Clashmore just across the Dornoch Firth from Tain. They are the most internationally famous of all Scottish traditional musicians and make a Highland tour every year, moving between often tiny village halls in a punishing schedule. Their concerts are always a sell-out.

Keeping genuine traditional music alive is an essential element of maintaining a distinctive Scottish cultural identity. Ostensibly, what Phil and Aly play is minority music and a long way from the ersatz Scottish music as presented by the populist tartan entertainers of the 1960s and '70s. And yet, as great performers, they have taken obscure and sometimes difficult music out into the world – in particular to America – while at the same time they have borrowed techniques from abroad. This will be their legacy. They both have MBEs; Phil has one honorary doctorate and Aly has four!

Aly and Phil have played the Carnegie Hall in New York as well as this more humble manifestation of Andrew Carnegie's remarkable philanthropy. They both proclaim a preference for Clashmore Carnegie Hall.

I was given Aly's mobile number by his agent, whom I know well, and phoned him. They were just off the Stornoway–Ullapool ferry but they agreed to a portrait that evening. It was damp and gloomy as they arrived at the hall and I made the portrait in about ten minutes. Or to be precise, about an hour to think about it and set up the camera and flash heads prior to their arrival. I stayed on for the concert, and while my tastes in music are not normally of the Scottish traditional kind, it was two hours of virtuoso music interspersed with tremendous entertainment. This was followed by the obligatory drinking. I don't know how they do it night after night. Confirming the rumour of Highland hospitality, I was strongly pressured to continue the party and stay over with two people, one of whom I knew from Edinburgh. I managed to persuade them that I was exhausted with a promise that I would call round for breakfast the next day. I climbed into the van, which was still outside the hall, set up the bed and was instantly comatose.

The following day, slow-witted and thick-headed, I went round for breakfast. It was loud company in a crowded kitchen. The gossip turned to Donald, who helps to organise events at the hall, and his girlfriend Angie, who is a police constable in Invergordon and is half-Scottish and half-West African. I was intrigued and thought that this might merit a portrait.

16

Craig and Anita Mackay, Brora

Pleased to be on the road again, I left Clashmore in good spirits and headed north amid intermittent sunshine and showers, with the intention of visiting my old friends Craig and Anita. Stopping at Dunrobin Castle near Golspie, I phoned them and received a typically warm welcome to stay.

Craig was born in Brora, and came to Napier University to study photography as a mature student several years ago. We met at his studio in a converted school on the outskirts of Brora before moving on to his house, where I had some difficulty parking the van among the dead or dying cars that Craig or Anita have owned over the years. Theirs is a rambling and cluttered eighteenth-century house that seems to exude open hospitality. Almost every piece of furniture in the whole building seems ancient, with the incongruous exception of a new kitchen extension that boasts the largest fridge I have ever seen. It even dispenses ice at the push of a button for the gin and tonic.

When Craig left Napier, I remember Anita phoning me at home, concerned about whether he would be able to make a living so far away from the media hub in the Central Belt – or London. He had never wanted to be a 'local' photographer doing weddings and such, but was keenly interested in editorial, advertising and 'fine art' work. I said then that it would be difficult . . .

Paradoxically the improvements in communications that have led to the atrophy of Highland communities have also meant that Craig as a Highlander can remain in Brora and travel where required much more easily than even 20 ago. As a photographer he can work for UK-wide clients, facilitated by the internet, email and mobile phones.

Anita is from Lewis, and she and Craig are both passionate about Highland culture, past and present – perhaps unusually so for indigenous Highlanders. Edwin Muir felt that he could not identify a specifically Scottish identity in 1934, but in the course of a long conversation over fantastic bowls of chicken and barley broth, Craig maintained that there was a Highland identity and that this resides in part in history: 'Culture doesn't invent itself – like a good whisky, it takes time to mature.' Amongst much else, we talked about communities and families and the disintegration of home-based entertainments brought about by the global influences via television and the internet. Craig put it down to 'heating, and the weather'. When he was young, his family would eat and converse together and then gather in the sitting room to watch *Z Cars* or play games in the only room that was warm. Now kids are in their bedrooms surfing the net and playing computer games.

17

Dunrobin Castle, Golspie

On my way north to Brora, I had stopped at Dunrobin and planned a picture that I might do there. I knew that if the sun was shining I needed to make the picture quite early in the morning. So it was that I left Craig and Anita (with the welcome gift of a couple of venison steaks) and drove the few miles south in wet and blustery weather. As I arrived at about 8.30 a.m. the sun intermittently appeared and I made the picture I had envisaged, pleased with my luck, and that I had correctly calculated the direction of the light.

This remarkable architectural confection and monumental icon of aristocratic land ownership still stands, for some, as a symbol for the Clearances, when tenant farmers were evicted and sent to the coast to take up fishing or emigrate while the land was turned over to the more profitable sheep. This still causes intense passions in the Highlands, where depopulation continued for the next 150 years. Equally passionate arguments continue amongst historians about whether the clearances were necessary economic improvements vindicated by history or a cruel and cynical exercise in social engineering motivated by profit.

The castle and estates are owned by the elderly Countess of Sutherland and managed by her son, Lord Strathnaver. They are descendants of the 1st Duke and Countess of Sutherland, who were ultimately responsible for the most notorious Clearances, particularly in Strathnaver. A massive monument to the 1st Duke stands on a hill above Golspie, erected 'by public subscription' in 1837, and there have been sporadic calls for its demolition as a monument to national disgrace and heartless evictions. But there he still stands, surveying hundreds of acres of land and sea that once belonged to him. No monuments to the evicted though, until one was erected at Helmsdale in 2007 – perpetrators usually do better than victims.

Besides a picture of Dunrobin, I had wanted to make a portrait of Lord Strathnaver, partly to gain an insight into contemporary issues of land tenure from a landowner's perspective. The previous evening Anita had suggested that I should phone the Sutherland Estates Office in Golspie and speak to Evelyn. This I did when I arrived back at the Tain campsite on my way south. Evelyn was polite, but guarded, and said that I should write to Lord Strathnaver, pointing out that he disliked being photographed. A little disappointed, I determined to write when back in Edinburgh.

In the event, despite a long and detailed letter establishing my credentials, followed by several phone calls to Evelyn and emails to the Estates Office, Lord Strathnaver did not reply, not even to instruct Evelyn to say 'no'. Perhaps there are vulnerable sensibilities here.

18

PC Angie Grant, Invergordon

The Tain campsite was apparently becoming my base for the north-east, and I spent the afternoon processing films before falling asleep while they dried. Thinking about a portrait of Angie Grant in Invergordon, I spent some time on the phone to Donald Munroe at Clashmore, who gave me Angie's number. I then phoned Angie and finally managed to organise a photograph for the next day, pleased to have a plan and not to be relying on chance encounters. So, unusually satisfied with a good day's work, I opened a bottle of wine, wrote in my journal, and fried Anita's gorgeous venison steaks.

The next day, I headed down to Invergordon, having arranged to meet Angie at 11 a.m., and found a possible location in the High Street, near the Jobcentre.

Industrial initiatives like Invergordon Smelter, Nigg and the deep-water haven brought workers, principally from Glasgow, to the north-east in the 1980s. These workers also brought urban social problems to this remote area, and towns like Alness and Invergordon have more than their fair share. As communities expand, urban ills pervade. Alcohol and other drug use is more prevalent among the young, and domestic theft, once unknown, is becoming more commonplace.

Angie Grant's mother is West African and her father is Scottish. She seemed to me to symbolise a multicultural Scotland, although she identifies strongly with a specifically Scottish culture. She wouldn't dream of living anywhere else. She's a 'beat' copper and the liaison officer for one of the primary schools. While I was setting up the camera she was chatting away to some kids, having a laugh. She was very easy-going and relaxed and seemed to know the name of every teenager that passed. She said that big ocean liners occasionally arrive in Invergordon. It's hardly a tourist trap though, and they get bussed quickly from there to Loch Ness or wherever.

Sitting in the van after making the portrait, I asked Angie about racial tension in the area and she said that it was rare, except for some Anglophobia: another social ailment within the Highlands and Islands community and indeed Scotland as a whole. This was hardly different from Muir's day – and perhaps, within the context of the Highlands, demonstrated by Muir himself. Repeatedly on this journey I felt a conflict between regretting the passing of a traditional culture and way of life, and celebrating the diversity of outlook that multiculturalism brings. And I mean multiculturalism to include Lowland Scots and English.

I left Invergordon at lunchtime and headed home to Edinburgh for respite, to review work so far, and to attempt a strategy for the west coast. The weather deteriorated steadily on the way, with hostile, glowering clouds over Drumochter, accompanied by wind and lashing rain. I was pleased, though, to be going home.

19

Biker, Tyndrum

I was seriously worried about my output of photographs at this stage. I had set myself a target of 50 finished pictures and had only produced about 25 – and that number would be severely edited. Muir relied on chance encounters and serendipity, but I had begun to realise that I would need to plan more precisely and identify Highland 'issues' that I wished to cover. As a photographer, I couldn't just wander around the Highlands pondering and then come back and write it all up. I had to photograph what was there. I also realised that I needed to seek out local knowledge, and people who knew people. Muir stayed in hotels and frequented tearooms throughout his journey and obviously met fellow travellers in the process (albeit reluctantly). I needed to socialise more, instead of just staying in the van in glorious isolation. Whole days could pass without my speaking to a soul.

I frequently regretted making the decision to use the large 5 × 4 camera – I missed a lot of pictures when, for example, the light changed before I could get the camera on the tripod. Or I would wonder whether it was worth valuable sheets of film and setting up the camera for a particular picture – only to regret not doing it at a later time. On a smaller format I would have just done it anyway. I did, however, want a certain kind of preconceived formality in the images, particularly the portraits, and I decided to stay with it. Paul Strand did OK with an even larger camera in South Uist in 1953. Mind you, he was there for three months.

With all this in mind and well rested, I set off for Ardnamurchan to visit my old friend Dominic Cooper.

It was a Saturday and the road was crowded with caravans and motorhomes; there were also large numbers of bikers, often several in a pack. These weekend bikers from both Glasgow and Edinburgh head off to burn up the roads and startle unsuspecting van drivers as they scream past at astonishing speeds. It was like being 'buzzed' by the RAF jets at Portmahomack. It's particularly a phenomenon of the west, rather than the A9, for some reason, and the Mecca for bikers seems to be Tyndrum, just north of Crianlarich where the A82 from Glasgow meets the A85 from Edinburgh.

Bikers were on my new list of photographs so I stopped at Tyndrum and attempted a portrait . . .

20

Dominic Cooper, writer and poet, Ardnamurchan

It was a long drive to Ardnamurchan from Edinburgh – about five hours – and the last hour and a half is on the peninsula itself, along tortuously twisty single-track roads. For some reason, when I had visited in the past with my wife Marjory and our son, we had always brought good weather with us, and this was no exception, with the bright, sharp light that the Highlands does so well – when it feels like it.

Many artists and writers have come to the Highlands to seek a more solitary and stress-free existence and to derive inspiration from the land. Dominic has lived here in a Norwegian log house for many years. He had struggled tenaciously for years before finally being granted planning permission – the authorities could not believe that it was not for a holiday home and that he intended to live and work there. It's quite unlike a traditional Highland house, which has thick walls and small rooms and windows. They are designed to keep out the wind and keep in the heat, and were 'fit for purpose' in Muir's day. But relatively modern technology has produced a design that is warm and light, open in design and still sympathetic to the landscape. The corrugation of the natural timber walls produces a reflected golden light and beautiful acoustics from even the most humble hi-fi system . . . Dominic's house, tucked out of sight of the road, feels good.

Dominic is the author of several highly regarded novels, although currently his main literary output is poetry. His inspiration has frequently come from remote Celtic cultures, usually from the distant past. Besides writing, he is a clock-repairer and he has a small workshop in his house.

It is still a mystery to me how Dominic survives psychologically, living there all the year round. Every time I see him I ask him that same question, to which I never seem to get a persuasive answer. Many of us – including me – have harboured romantic notions of a solitary life in remote areas, particularly after a summer holiday there, of rest and relaxation, but the reality is obviously quite different. I remember Dominic telling me that after an insistently dismal winter that dragged on well into April even the locals were succumbing to symptoms of depression.

Generally, Dominic does not engage much with the community, and despite the fact that he could now be termed a 'local' he generally avoids involving himself or meddling in local affairs. The only thing that has galvanised him politically is the wind-farm issue, and he even agreed to hand out leaflets on the Corran ferry.

John Dobson's wind turbine, Kilmory, Ardnamurchan

Dominic and I discussed the wind-farm issue at length. This has been the cause of passionate debate for some years throughout Scotland but particularly in the Highlands. There is an acknowledged need for alternative, sustainable green energy sources and few would argue with that in principle. But it's a great paradox of wind energy that a technology designed to reduce carbon emissions, and so mitigate climate change, can be destructive to the immediate environment. Many have said that the turbines are actually quite beautiful and indeed even quite large ones have a certain awesome and powerful attraction. Dominic maintained, however, that it is important to imagine 400 of them, each the size of Big Ben, ranged along the slopes of Ben Hiant. Then there is the infrastructure required to build them – jetties and roads to be built, and the enormous pylons required to take the electricity off the peninsula – not east to Fort William, or even to Glasgow, but to Birmingham. Local people would not benefit from the immense disruption, except perhaps for a few who would gain short-lived employment in construction. However, landowners – many of whom are absentee – stand to make small fortunes in the sale of the land. Besides that, there is a great deal of money to be made through construction, and political capital to be made playing the increasingly populist green card. There seems to be a lot of vested interests in wind farms, which makes one sceptical of the expensive studies commissioned to prove the environmental and economic benefits.

Dominic was quite emphatic that he would have to leave if the wind farms came . . .

John Dobson lives a few miles from Dominic in the old school house at Branault. When electricity came to the area, the power line passed close to the back of the house but his father refused to be connected. John taught himself the mechanics and the electronics of building his own wind turbine.

Perhaps one answer to the whole wind-farm issue is to build on a more domestic scale for a local population. And if the government is serious about promoting green energy, more extensive – and realistic – grants and subsidies should be provided for communities and individuals.

Electricity supply, Kilmory, Ardnamurchan

This part of north-west Ardnamurchan seemed particularly remote and I found myself becoming increasingly introspective with decreasing human contact. The four miles of single-track road that passes below Dominic's house dead-ends at a farm, so there is no through traffic. There have been occasional plans to extend the road east to Acharacle, thereby creating a circular route, but so far (to Dominic's relief) this has not happened.

Staying near to Dominic's house, I spent a grey day processing film and scanning negatives, occasionally starting the van's engine to ensure that my laptop and scanner weren't draining the battery. Aware that I could quite easily spend the whole day without seeing a soul, I drove into Kilchoan and bought some sausages and salad for tea, while making a mental note that I really needed to extend and improve my diet. On the way back, the sun struggled to make an appearance, and finally provided a marvellous view of Eigg and Rum. Invigorated by the early evening light, I climbed a gentle hill and made a picture.

Electricity came to Kilmory in the late 1970s and I suppose that its spread to all except the most remote communities was a great enabler. As a city-based person, it's hard to imagine a life without the telephone and the conveniences that electricity brings. In particular, followed by television and the internet, it has facilitated communications over the last few decades. This has meant that a broader range of employment opportunities has opened up, including working from home; but it has also signalled a decline in close-knit communities. Television especially has led to an increase in external influences that have not always been positive, and in part has led to a dumbing-down and debasement of Highland culture.

That evening I had a final dinner with Dominic after quite unreasonable anxiety about negotiating the van up his precipitous road. We had beautifully cooked scallops, a pastry-based flan with tomatoes and stilton, and excellent wine. In the course of the conversation, Dominic suggested that I take a look at an abandoned village that he had frequently visited on Mull and which was the basis for his acclaimed novel *The Dead of Winter*. I hadn't planned a visit to Mull, but this sounded sufficiently interesting to make the diversion.

Cragaig, north-west Mull

I caught the 10.15 a.m. ferry from Kilchoan to Tobermory the following day. The weather had changed again to a fine drizzle as I stopped on the colourful waterfront to pick up petrol and water for the van and provisions for its occupant. Sadly it was too early to sample fish and chips at the Egon Ronay-rated fish van on the pier. I headed up the west coast and decided to wild camp at Calgary, seduced by its glorious beach and in the hope that the weather would improve the following day.

Thunderous rain woke me the next morning at 4.30 a.m. as it pummelled the roof of the van and I instantly felt sorry for my fellow campers in tents who had been trying to dry socks on guy ropes the previous evening. There being no point in attempting to catch early morning light, I allowed myself to fall asleep again, finally heading off late morning round fiendish cliff-top bends to the start of the track to Cragaig. The rain had abated to a gentle smirr and I decided optimistically to set off on the two-mile walk.

This tiny village was abandoned, not due to the Clearances, as so many were, but voluntarily, when the plague arrived from Ireland. Much later, when I was back in Edinburgh, Dominic wrote to me in an email:

'Maybe Cragaig itself is not important except as a representation of all the emptied Highlands. That beautifully built wall and corner which, at the time, was a skill of such necessity. Its beauty of line is much more than beauty for beauty's sake: a beauty that was man's vital attempt to dovetail himself into the harsher beauties of nature – for the corner of the building is both tapered and rounded so as to take the wind. The abandonment of these 'remote' world centres may be seen as the beginning of the abandonment of community, and of the self as part of community; as the beginning of the modern individual's obsession with self and all material things. I have always felt that the loss of this community bonding, as well as the loss of our earthing in the soil, was the beginning of the disintegration of all natural happiness. And was the beginning of the necessity for psychiatrists.'

The photograph I made was of the house that Dominic chose for Alasdair Mor, the main protagonist in *The Dead of Winter.*

Returning to Calgary, wet and dispirited by the weather, I determined to leave early the next morning and head up the west coast towards Shieldaig and Applecross.

24

Laggan Dam

Driving north through Fort William I thought back to the conundrum of sustainable energy: simply put, the need for green energy versus the impact on the landscape, ecology, and wildlife. I decided to make a short detour off the A82 to Laggan Dam. It turned out to be a beautifully clear Highland morning which lifted the spirits and seemed to demand that photographs be taken. Parking at the dam, I made some coffee, and set the camera on the tripod.

Hydro-electricity is the most established form of renewable energy in Scotland and has in the past been criticised by environmentalists for its impact on aquatic life and, in initial construction, the landscape. But since the widely acknowledged need for reducing carbon emissions and with the wind power debate, this has abated.

Laggan Dam was completed in 1934, the same year that Muir made his journey, and well before hydro-electricity was nationalised in 1948. Situated four miles west of Loch Laggan, the dam was built by the British Aluminium Company to provide hydro-electricity for their aluminium smelter at Inverlochy near Fort William. The dam crosses the River Spean, harnessing the waters of Loch Laggan. Water runs by tunnel to Loch Treig and thence by 15 miles of underground tunnel before descending through pipes down the shoulder of Ben Nevis.

A new hydro-electric system is being built nearby on the eastern side of Loch Ness, which will be the first major construction for 40 years. Full consultation has taken place with environmental groups and the dam will feed water to an underground power station near Fort Augustus. Many claim that this is a more efficient and reliable form of renewable energy than wind farms – and less of a threat to bird life.

I loitered at Laggan longer than I should have, idly watching tourists from Italy, France and Germany in cars, motorhomes and on bicycles stop, take snaps in the warm sunshine, and move on. And so, after a while, did I, to rejoin the A82 north.

25

Loch Garry

Diverting off the A82 at Invergarry, I took the road towards Kyle of Lochalsh. The weather was holding up – actually quite hot – and although by this time the sun was climbing too high in the sky for good landscape photography, I stopped by the banks of Loch Garry. Sometimes it's just too difficult to ignore and I allowed myself the luxury of languishing in the warmth, and the undemanding pleasures of picture-making for its own sake.

This is why so many people are attracted to the Highlands, of course: the simple pleasure of gazing and the internal strength and spiritual uplift to be gained. I met one couple from Bolton who were in the Highlands for the first time in an old VW campervan. They were simply astonished by the landscape . . .

I suppose that the human spirit needs these wild and solitary places, even if it doesn't know it. But they can imbue a sense of melancholy along with introspection. This despondency arises in part from the fact that there are now so few 'unspoilt' places, and those that exist are continually under threat. The romantically inclined photographer finds it increasingly difficult to make pictures of the unblemished picturesque and such pictures are really complicit in a deceit. In retrospect, I was aware that I had framed this picture to exclude a dump of plastic bottles and that I had removed an empty cigarette packet.

In addition, there is for me an inherent problem with this type of landscape photography that attempts to express romantic notions of the sublime or the beautiful. While a record of the geography is interesting in a limited sort of way, it will always fail in communicating a real sense of awe because one will always prefer the place itself. I have a photographer friend who loves Highland landscape, but who rarely photographs it because he knows that while moved by the experience, a photograph can only fail to communicate what he felt, heard and smelt, as well as saw.

Looking out over the water I was reminded of one of the 'Detached Sentences' by the poet Ian Hamilton Finlay: 'The most pleasing aspect of water, strange to say, is its flatness.' To which one might riposte that the most unpleasant aspect of calm water is the Highland midge.

26

K.C. Mackinnon, sheepdog trials, Strathcarron

Finally and reluctantly heading on again, I turned off at the A890 intending to stay at Shieldaig, for which I have a great affection and used to visit regularly. Passing Strathcarron there were signs advertising the 'Country Day' and sheepdog trials to take place the next day. It was my birthday and my wife Marjory was meeting me at the campsite in Shieldaig so I could allow myself the rest of the day off from worrying about photography.

It's a free campsite with splendid views over the pretty village and Shieldaig Island. I settled in and looked forward to seeing Marjory and having dinner in the excellent Tigh an Eilean Hotel. And first rate it was, if rather expensive.

The next day we breakfasted on wonderful, fresh, amber-yolked eggs from Lochcarron Stores, and then went over to Strathcarron. I don't think I have ever been to a sheepdog trial where it hasn't rained and this was no exception but, despite that, spirits seemed high with everyone. There were a lot of the country set there in Range Rovers, but besides them and the tourists, the predominant accent was West Highland. While these events are popular with visitors, they still represent an important event and focus for the community, with a variety of other activities taking place including wool-dyeing and stick-making. As usual, Marjory proved to be a great antidote to my shyness and was soon engaging a variety of locals in conversation – including some shepherds. She's a social emollient, and I frequently wished she had accompanied me on the whole journey – a useful accessory indeed for the documentary photographer.

Naturally these are working dogs and it has been said that without the particularly intelligent Border Collie there would be no sheep industry in the Highlands. I wasn't quite sure how I felt about that, given the tragic history of the Clearances, when people were replaced with sheep. Apparently a trained sheepdog can sell for up to £6,000 and despite technology in the form of quad bikes, they are still indispensable.

Shepherds come from all over the Highlands and Islands to these trials, which take place in several locations over the summer months. They probably started unofficially in the Borders and came to the Highlands in the late nineteenth century. This is K.C. Mackinnon with his dogs, Bob and Corrie, over from Skye. I don't think anybody knows what his first name actually is . . .

Marjory bought some wool and I bought a stick – noting carefully from the shepherds their technique of leaning on it while engaging in casual conversation.

27

Musicians, Applecross

Marjory left for Edinburgh the following morning and I went on to Applecross with only vague plans of what I might do. I did, however, want to renew my acquaintance with the peerless Applecross Inn. I booked into the reasonably priced campsite and then walked down to the village to buy some supplies, retreating to the van for a relaxed afternoon indoors with a gale blowing up outside. That evening I returned to the village and called at the inn, still run, I was pleased to see, by Judith Fish who I think has been there since the late 1980s. It's a small inexpensive hotel with a warm and friendly atmosphere. Most Highland hotels have a lounge bar and a public bar, the former for hotel guests and the latter for locals, but in Judith's inn there is no hierarchy. I ordered a pint, chatted to the Irish barmaid and was pleased to see that there was to be music that night from 'Sean and Helena'. In the event, they didn't play, for reasons that weren't at all clear although they were sitting in the bar. Nevertheless, thinking that a photograph might be worthwhile and rather wishing that Marjory was still with me, I went over to introduce myself. We agreed to make a portrait the following morning.

They are Sean KilBride and Helena Torpy. She's from Bristol and has a friend who was born in Applecross and at that time was working in the hotel. Sean was born in Applecross, moved away, and then moved back to the area recently. They play guitar and fiddle respectively.

A sense of community and Highland cultural identity resides partly in music and the social arts. This is found not just in the tours by well-known performers like Phil and Aly, but in local talent gathering for ceilidhs in homes, bars and village halls. Very much like the Gaelic language, it seems essential to me that these skills – particularly fiddle and bagpipe – are passed down within the family, as well as being taught as a formal part of the school curriculum.

The next morning was dreich – that insistent and impenetrable drizzle so tediously typical of the north-west. Just before Sean and Helena appeared outside the Inn, the weather cleared sufficiently to make the portrait. Not an immensely satisfactory experience on the whole – I only briefly made their acquaintance and I didn't even hear them play. . .

28

The Charity family, Ardindrean, Loch Broom

I decided to take the coastal road north and stopped at Poolewe campsite to catch up on processing films, a little bit happier that my output of work was improving slightly. Really by this time, I preferred wild camping, but I needed a plentiful supply of water for processing, and running the laptop and scanner was easier when there was an electric hook-up. Determining that I needed some more local knowledge and to engage in more 'serious' research, I phoned my old friends John and Celia Charity in Ullapool who, even at that short notice, said they would be happy for me to stay.

So the following day I meandered towards Ullapool and, at last firmly back on Muir's route, arrived at about 6 p.m. and parked the van beside their croft house on the west bank of Loch Broom. John is a highly respected documentary photographer and I used to teach with him many years ago. Since he and Celia moved to the area 26 years ago, I see far too little of them.

Muir saw incomers – at that time principally from England – as representing an erosion of Scottish identity, even in the 1930s. John and Celia Charity came to Loch Broom from the Midlands and have totally embraced the local community and Gaelic culture – much more so than some locals. John took a degree in Gaelic at Aberdeen University some years ago and has been instrumental in setting up the Gaelic unit in Ullapool. They had recently obtained the tenancy of their croft and have a couple of pigs, about 50 sheep and some hens. It is virtually impossible to make a living out of crofting alone, however, so like most crofters, they both have other jobs. John now works for Scottish Natural Heritage and Celia paints and looks after the children with a part-time job in a shop in Ullapool. In addition they had recently begun to offer bed and breakfast to bring in a little extra cash. Their eldest son Seonaidh had just started a degree in philosophy and Gaelic at Glasgow University. There is a strong sense here that they have not simply parachuted into a different culture and immediately told locals how they should be running their lives (as has been the accusation heard so often on my journey), but that they have genuinely integrated into a different way of life and have worked hard to sustain what they saw as a culture under threat.

After making a portrait of the whole family, and over an enjoyable dinner, John provided several suggestions of whom I might speak to about Gaelic culture, crofting and so on. With guests upstairs for bed and breakfast, I retreated to the van and made good use of an electric hook-up extended through their sitting room window. I was close enough to benefit from their wi-fi reception and reluctantly checked a multitude of emails on the laptop.

29

Dyke, Loch Broom

I woke the following morning with a thicker head than usual, thanks to the liberal consumption of John's Macallan whisky. John had suggested I contact Jean Urquhart, who runs the Ceilidh Place in Ullapool. I had met her with John on previous visits so I phoned and she agreed to meet for coffee the next morning. Pleased that I had a plan, I set off for Ullapool and stopped halfway along the east side of the loch.

From the outset of my journey, and for reasons that I was not quite clear about, I'd had an idea that I would like to photograph a dry-stone dyke – certainly they are beautiful objects and are very much part of Highland history and landscape. It was, however, the only preconceived image that I had, and I had been continually looking out for one that was suitably interesting photographically, accessible, and unaccompanied by fencing, which is relatively rare.

Dry-stone dykes were, historically, the predominant field boundaries where rocky outcrops, thin soils and climate made the use of hedgerows impractical. Built without mortar, these sturdy walls provide habitat for small animals, lichens and mosses. They can last up to 200 years if the stones aren't pinched for other uses, but they are decaying and declining because fences are much cheaper and quicker to erect. This in turn has meant that dykeing is a dying craft.

As part of agricultural improvements in the late eighteenth and nineteenth century, and the coming of sheep after the Clearances, land was often enclosed. There must be hundreds of miles of dykes in the Highlands and these beautiful and functional sculptural 'installations' are a triumph of skill and labour. They could be considered the pinnacle of land art, and Scottish artists like Ian Hamilton Finlay and Andy Goldsworthy have both made their own tributes to the art of the dry-stone dyker.

Satisfied that I had made a picture so early in the day, I continued into Ullapool to buy some whisky to replenish John's stock and to browse the bookshops in this agreeable port. Later, drinking coffee in the van, a light drizzle started as I wondered which of the hotels Muir might have stayed in: the Caledonian surely. Consulting his *Scottish Journey*, I found this in his description of his stay in Ullapool: 'I walked up and down the pier for some time until I found a run of wooden steps leading down to an underground gallery almost level with the sea. There, protected from the rain, I walked about for a long time, listening to the drip of the water from the planks overhead and the murmur of the tide as it sluggishly flowed round the rotting piles . . . The water dripped, filling the little gallery with tiny echoes that sounded like shivering glass. I do not know why, but soft rain in the Highlands makes them seem twice as remote, so that one cannot imagine they are within reach of anywhere.'

30

Jean Urquhart, The Ceilidh Place, Ullapool

I arrived at the Ceilidh Place the next morning at 11 a.m. and Jean and I had coffee outside in warm sunshine. A well-known personality in the Highlands, she has owned and run one of the best small hotels in Scotland since 1970. She is also an SNP councillor and was awarded an MBE for Services to the Arts. I had stayed at the Ceilidh Place on a few occasions before, and had always felt at home here. It doesn't have Scottish Tourist Board rating because the rooms don't have televisions, trouser presses or wrapped soap. Instead they have a selection of books suggested by well-known writers who have stayed there regularly. There is a spacious, comfortable lounge supplied with tea and coffee to which guests may help themselves, and an honesty bar. Importantly, it has good food and an excellent, eclectic bookshop. This is a place where the arts and culture are central.

We talked about most of the major issues facing the Highlands. She was sceptical about fish farming and felt it was a money-making industry where the salmon are penned in and don't have the benefit of the annual struggle upriver. Jean felt that some of the fish should be put into the sea to replenish stocks. However, she mentioned a couple of fish farms in the north-west and Orkney where good practice was being implemented.

On the subject of tourism, she was clearly passionate about her hotel and she thought that tourism had become an impersonal industry with statistical benchmarks instead of something more individual. Tourist board officials frequently opt to stay in her hotel despite the fact that it is not rated. Tourism is economically very important to the Highlands, and while over the last few years the hotel and catering trade has improved, it has been my experience that standards are still generally poor, with often inexperienced and curmudgeonly service. Only recently could you get a decent cup of coffee with fresh milk, for example. There is definitely a friendly and vibrant atmosphere about Jean's hotel, however.

Jean felt strongly that a separate Scottish identity exists and that it is defined by culture. In particular she felt that the arts principally determine any national identity and it was clear that she does an immense amount to promote arts in the hotel, with visual art exhibitions and regular concerts.

We talked a lot about incomers and in particular overseas workers in the hotel, and she readily agreed to organise some of her workers for the next day. Meanwhile, I managed to persuade her to meet a little later, so that I could make a portrait in the lounge.

Immigrant workers, The Ceilidh Place, Ullapool

The next morning I returned to the Ceilidh Place and set up a picture at the kitchen door of the hotel. As Jean promised, she had organised three workers for me who could spare a few minutes.

Multiculturalism is an increasing characteristic of even the most remote parts of the Highlands. There has been an influx of foreign workers, especially East European, since the European Union suddenly grew in 2004 by ten countries, most of them economically poor. Throughout my journey I encountered East Europeans everywhere I went, although I was never quite clear how, for example, somebody from eastern Poland could end up in Bettyhill.

The hotel trade in the Highlands has long relied on immigrant seasonal workers, and Jean maintained that she felt privileged to have so many young people from different cultures working for her. In the 1970s it was Filipinos, in the '80s and '90s it was mainly Australians and New Zealanders working to finance a holiday or on a gap year from university; now it's Eastern Europeans, but they come for economic reasons. She had one kitchen worker from Poland who had professional parents (his father was a surgeon), and this lad earned more than his parents. Other than when her chefs get a bit irritated with occasional language problems, she sees her overseas workers as a definite asset. We both agreed that while it was essential that Highland culture is maintained and encouraged, it would be dreadful if Scotland were only populated by Scots! As I write, it seems that immigration from these new EU countries is slowing, and indeed some workers are returning to their native countries. This will inevitably signal a dangerous gap in the employment market – especially in hospitality and catering, and in jobs that some Scots are reluctant to do.

After packing up my equipment, I headed back to browse the bookshop and bought a copy of *We Have Won the Land* by John MacAskill. I'd had a long discussion with John Charity about the land tenure issue, and the Assynt Crofters' Trust was definitely on my list of potential subjects.

A last pleasant evening with John, Celia and the boys, and armed with some useful contacts, I planned to go over to Stornoway the next day.

Ola Witkowska, *receptionist*, Poland
Stefan Laktis, *chef*, Slovakia
Cyril Mkhize (OB), *kitchen porter*, South Africa

Dr Finlay MacLeod, Shawbost,
Isle of Lewis

I caught the 9.30 a.m. ferry from Ullapool and decided to have a MacBraynes hearty breakfast which I was soon to regret, as the crossing became particularly rough and I spent almost two hours sitting rigid, listening to passengers being sick. I hadn't realised that people make quite so much noise when throwing up – a sound strongly reminiscent of John's pigs.

I found Stornoway's campsite, processed some films and tried to organise portraits of a couple of the contacts that John had given me. In the event I was on Lewis for three days before managing to make one picture.

I phoned my friend, the photographer Murdo MacLeod, who lives in Edinburgh but is from Shawbost, and he suggested (as had John Charity), that I speak to Finlay MacLeod as someone with extensive knowledge of Lewis and its history. Finlay and his wife Norma are both native Gaelic speakers and writers.

Finlay agreed with Jean Urquhart that national identity is created in part by culture, but he maintained that it is also established by language and *place* – the land. Lewis is identifiably Lewis, as is Edinburgh and so on. This is why he is so against the industrial scale of wind farms – or 'wind factories' as they are called on Lewis by those who oppose them. Much like Dominic Cooper on Ardnamurchan, he said that if anything would drive him out, it would be taking the land away from him.

One of Finlay's long-standing concerns is the globalisation of the vernacular architecture. He maintained that the black house was fitting for its purpose and blended with the landscape. It would, however, be a mistake to indulge in nostalgia: crofters lived in appalling conditions in the early disease-ridden black houses. No attempt has been made to develop the black house for modern society. Instead a completely different style has been erected and now unattractive 1960s-style bungalows are all over Lewis. These kit houses are cheap and easily erected, but it must be possible to design a house that is both affordable for a local population and sympathetic to the land.

Finlay is politically active in promoting Gaelic, which he sees as an essential ingredient of Hebridean identity. At a cultural level it's relatively healthy – and both he and his wife Norma write in Gaelic – but it is really only woven into the fabric of society when it is spoken at a domestic level, and the danger is that soon it will not be.

Lewis is staunchly Free Church, and I was slightly surprised that Finlay intensely dislikes it. Besides taking issue with its fundamentalist Calvinist beliefs, he feels that it has had undue control over people's lives and that the last vestige of that is Sabbatarianism. Perhaps, however, there is a paradox here: historically the Free Church championed ordinary people against landowners (after 1843), which the Established Church did not. And it has also done a great deal to preserve the Gaelic language.

33

Barvas Moor, Isle of Lewis

Driving back to Stornoway from my meeting with Finlay, I crossed Barvas Moor, where it is proposed that hundreds of turbines would be sited. It's a fast, straight and relatively flat road, and as I finally managed to find a place to stop and make a photograph, cars tore past as if they were keen to spend as little time as possible in this austere place.

The wind-farm issue has tragically split Lewis opinion. There are strong feelings on both sides but a vast majority in Lewis seem to be against the proposal, which would change the landscape and their lives for ever. It is proposed that Barvas Moor be home to the largest wind farm ever, with the biggest possible turbines, each considerably higher than the Forth Bridge. Some people feel that it would be no great loss to establish turbines on a remote place like Barvas Moor and that it would enhance the economy, while others – especially local crofters – are against what they see as physical and cultural desecration. Powerful environmental groups like the Royal Society for the Protection of Birds are also strongly against the proposal. Broadly speaking, the issues and arguments are similar to those related to the proposed wind farms on Ardnamurchan.

It seems to me that it must be difficult for those living in the south of Scotland or in England to care much what happens to a desolate moor on Lewis. They would see only the financial benefits and what are seen as the advantages of 'green' energy despite the high levels of carbon dioxide that would be released back into the atmosphere if the peatlands are drained.

But I was deeply moved by the passionate arguments made by Finlay MacLeod and others that I spoke to. If nothing else, establishment of a 'wind factory' on the scale proposed, with its extensive infrastructure, is an environmentally irreversible step and I wondered, if it were to happen, how it would be judged by posterity.

As I write, the issue is still unresolved, although the original proposal has been scaled down – so while the Moorlands Without Turbines lobby has won a limited victory, there is still a long way to go.

Returning to the campsite I phoned another contact given to me by John Charity, Niall Iain Macdonald, a DJ with Radio Alba. He agreed to a photograph and said that he was helping with a rock festival (Trees in the Park) at Cuddy Point in Stornoway that evening. Rather reluctantly I went down at 5 p.m. and the first person I met was Niall Iain. We arranged to do to a portrait at Radio Alba the next morning and meanwhile I managed to make a couple of pictures of teenagers, including one of a boy in a Nicholson Institute blazer and ragged jeans.

34

Niall Iain Macdonald, Stornoway

Lewis is the heartland of both the Free Church and the Gaelic language, and was the only place in Scotland where I had heard Gaelic spoken regularly in the street. Place names are provided in Gaelic as well as English in most of the Highlands, but here the Gaelic takes precedence over English and the type is much larger. Stornoway hosts the BBC's Radio Nan Gaidheal, its Gaelic radio station. As Finlay MacLeod had said, for Gaelic to survive it has to be spoken round the kitchen table – and by the young. I had also heard it said, though, that there is an element of cultural snobbery amongst the Gaelic community and that it needs to welcome all who would wish to learn the language. Niall Iain plays mainstream rock music on his popular programme *Rapal* – but his commentary is in Gaelic.

Stornoway was closed – the centre was totally deserted except for churchgoers passing by as I guiltily set up the camera and lights before Niall Iain arrived. This is the Sabbatarianism of the Free Church – no shops open, except for one petrol station on the outskirts that opens for a few hours in the afternoon. Even the excellent arts centre, An Lanntair, was closed. I had intended to leave Stornoway that day, but no ferries run on a Sunday. To be honest, I found Stornoway a drab and listless town. Certainly this may have been due to generally gloomy weather, but I had noticed frequently in cafés and public spaces, leaflets offering help for alcoholism and depression. The Western Isles has Scotland's highest male unemployment and highest suicide rate, mainly amongst young men. This is sometimes attributed to a closed and macho culture in Highland men, and the pages of the *Stornoway Gazette* – especially the eccentric 'Police Files' section – is testament to a fair amount of drunken brawling on Friday and Saturday nights.

I was later to discover that Niall Iain, handsome, friendly and popular as he was (and is), had also acknowledged his own problems, and as I write he has just completed a remarkable sponsored row of the Minch, a solitary and punishing 43 miles in aid of charities including the Western Isles Association For Mental Health.

I returned to the campsite for my last night (as I thought) in Stornoway, relieved that I had enough food in the van for my tea. The midges were out, infesting a murky and heavy evening, and out too were some campers wearing midge nets, looking for all the world like visitors from Porton Down.

That evening I processed two batches of film and discovered that the shutter had malfunctioned on the photograph I did of the boy at the rock concert. I had had high hopes for it as a picture and, dispirited by that and other technical problems, I decided that I needed a break. I'd return to Edinburgh, get the lens serviced, see Marjory – and have a decent bath.

35

Ewan Armstrong, Stornoway

I spent a few days back in Edinburgh, had the lens repaired, and decided impulsively to reshoot the boy I'd met at the rock concert. I had contact details for everyone I photographed on my journey, so I phoned him and he was very happy to do another picture. So it was a very early start, and up the road again heading straight for Ullapool. I had decided not to take the van over to Stornoway, and parked it near to the ferry terminal, going over as a foot passenger and planning an overnight stay in a hotel.

We arranged to meet late afternoon, and I decided to do a picture at what seemed to be a gathering place for teenagers in the centre. Ewan is a rock musician, and at 25 was older than I first thought. His stage name is Ryder James and he gave me a CD of his music which, far from Gaelic influences, was mainly covers of mainstream rock music by artists like Jeff Buckley. I was pleased to see that he was dressed exactly as he was at Cuddy Point a fortnight before. His jacket was the local school blazer – that of the Nicholson Institute.

Globalisation has brought a conformity of dress and life attitudes to young people everywhere, but there are always those who wilfully assert their individuality. That's relatively easy to do in a city, but in a small town like Stornoway he must have felt quite marginalised. I wondered how long he would stay before moving to a city where difference is more readily tolerated. Generally in the Highlands, and particularly the Western Isles, the population has steadily and remorselessly fallen – and is ageing. Young people have tended to move out, and not just because of high unemployment caused by very little industry and the decline in fishing. In Ewan's case, I suspect that he had firmly rejected the Hebridean Gaelic culture that he was brought up in, and certainly the discipline and influence of the Free Church.

That evening, dank and overcast, Stornoway seemed particularly dejected. After booking into the Royal Hotel, I had an indifferent meal in an otherwise empty Balti House, followed by a pint in the dismal Clachan Bar served by a cheery Pole. I was looking forward to getting back to the mainland the next day, to the van, and to continuing north. With hotel and ferry expenses, that had been an expensive photograph.

36

Allan MacRae, crofter, North Lochinver

Arriving in Ullapool on the early ferry, I filled up with diesel, shopped in the supermarket, and then headed north, stopping at the Ardmair campsite. I had talked at length to John Charity about the whole land-tenure issue in the Highlands, and he had suggested a couple of people I should talk to. So I spent a quiet day phoning various contacts and reading the book I had bought in the Ceilidh Place about the Assynt Crofters' Trust. It's emotive stuff.

The next day, I drove to Lochinver, having arranged a meeting with Claire Belshaw, who is active in the Assynt Foundation. It manages 40,000 acres, including Suilven, with a view to protecting and sustaining the natural environment and traditional industries. Her house in North Lochinver had been her holiday home but she and her family had moved up permanently about ten years previously. She was very informative about the complicated and ever-changing crofting and land-tenure legislation.

Enormous areas of the Highlands are owned by relatively few (often absentee) landowners. In 1992 Allan MacRae and two other crofters formed the Assynt Crofters' Trust and after a colossal struggle to raise funds, made land history by purchasing the North Lochinver Estate from its owner. This marked the beginning of a series of crofter, and then community, buy-outs of privately owned estates.

The Assynt Foundation was the result of the 2003 Land Reform Act, which determined that the government would assist *communities* to buy the land – not just crofters. Clearly tensions have arisen between ACT and AF. We talked about incomers like her, who work on behalf of the community, and the occasional antipathy that they were subject to, even though they bring skills to bear that 'locals' may not have.

Leaving Claire, I decided to drive up to the viewpoint above Achmelvich and phoned Allan MacRae, who is now chairman of the ACT. He said he would come up to the viewpoint and see me straight away. I wasn't expecting to see him so immediately and would have preferred to plan the picture more carefully, but managed to hurriedly set up the camera with the lumpen brooding mass of Suilven in the background. After making his portrait, we sat in the van and, over a dram, with a thick West Highland accent, he told me about his disappointment with the 2003 Land Reform Act, which allows for a 'hostile' takeover of crofting land even where the landowner does not wish to sell. 'We've seen off the landlords but the politicians have replaced landlords . . . we've no friends amongst politicians now.' Allan maintained that there should be 'self-determination' for crofters and that communities should not be allowed to tell them how to run their crofts. 'Why should the crofters hand over their land to everybody in the community? Socialist dogma!'

37

Esther Brauer, post office, Kylesku

After a contented night at Achmelvich near to a beautiful white-sanded beach, I retraced my route east along Loch Assynt rather than take the more tortuous coastal route round North Lochinver. Just before Inchnadamph, I rejoined Muir's road north towards Kylesku. It was a pleasantly sunny day, the van was driving well, and spirits were high as I left the main road ten miles further on and parked near the pier at Kylesku.

Muir too was blessed with sunshine as he stopped there to wait three hours for the tide to board the ferry north. His elderly car had not been running well and he calculated that he must have only managed six miles an hour since leaving Ullapool, over increasingly difficult roads 'little better than cart-tracks'. He must have been frustrated by the wait. Interestingly, he comments that 'except for two or three huts beside the ferry there was not a human habitation in sight' and yet a stone plaque on the Kylesku Hotel, right by the old ferry slipway, says it was built in 1883 – and the crow-step gables and stone construction testify to this. Strange; Muir must have forgotten when he wrote up his *Journey*, in London some months later. There are much better roads now, and no ferry, but there is a splendid bridge, opened in 1984, one of many new bridges in the Highlands, improving communications and shortening journeys north. The old two-car ferry is still there, a rotting hulk pulled up on the shore across the bay.

Besides the hotel and, for the itinerant, the very convenient public conveniences, there was a tiny post office at the side of a house, typical of many in the Highlands. Wandering in, I asked the owner if I might take a picture . . .

Esther Brauer has been the postmistress at Kylesku for 54 years. She is married to a German (Walter) who came 'during the war', and it was a second marriage for both of them. She is a West Highlander and her family have lived in the area for generations. She has a poodle called Toby which seems to be a source of amusement with other locals who presumably prefer the more common country dogs like collies. She was worried that the post office might close due to the cuts that were gradually insinuating themselves into rural areas and that this signalled a further disintegration of the community. With true Highland hospitality she invited me in for coffee, wonderful homemade cake and chat. Time and again I hear about these wee places being ghost towns in the winter with too many holiday homes. And some incomers stay for a while 'but don't last the winter . . .'

38

Fish-farm workers, Badcall, Scourie

Leaving Kylesku I crossed the high majestic curve of the new bridge and after a few miles found myself at Scourie, where I booked into a pleasant campsite with an open aspect facing the sea, just a short walk from the Scourie Hotel.

Scourie was still largely recognisable from Muir's description and it was easy to imagine his presence there. Customarily he described the physical nature of places he stopped at, along with people he met in hotels, but didn't really comment on local issues like economy or employment at all. I liked Scourie; it had a pleasant ambience, small but open, and with a good hotel as a focal point. Muir stayed here on his fifth night in the Highlands.

I had determined to make a picture of fish farmers, and Jean Urquhart had said that she felt one of the best in terms of environmental sustainability was Loch Duart fish farm just south of Scourie. Fish farming is one of the fastest growing sectors of the world food economy, especially in the Highlands, but the whole issue of aquaculture causes strong debate over its impact on Scotland's fragile marine environment.

After a shave and a cup of coffee I drove back to Badcall to meet the production manager Mark Woods, a friendly Englishman, and he agreed to organise a couple of crew members for me to photograph the next morning at 8 a.m.

That evening I treated myself to a rare meal out in the hotel, which was an excellent 'Kinlochbervie' haddock and chips in an almost empty bar – except for a local lad, sitting in the corner morosely nursing a pint of Guinness and a severe nasal problem. After a while two Englishmen appeared, loudly ordering 'two pints of Stella!' and then disappearing into the restaurant area, yapping inconsequentially at an indiscreet volume. Muir would have disapproved . . .

Retreating to the van for whisky and coffee, I loaded film holders for an early start the next morning. I had a really bad night's sleep, waking at 2.30 a.m. with rain splattering like a snare drum on the plastic skylight, and I dozed fitfully in between worrying about the picture. I started awake in a panic at 7 a.m., hastily packed away the bed and made off to Badcall with the weather thankfully improving. Mark Woods was true to his word and two Highland crewmen were waiting for me. Pleasant and laconic (I liked that), they waited patiently and slightly bemused as I set the camera and adjusted the flash.

Feeling rather self-satisfied that I had made a picture before breakfast, I returned to Scourie for a leisurely coffee, did some shopping in the local store and moved on.

James Forsyth, *senior skipper*
Duncan Morrison, *crewman*

39

Kinlochbervie, north-west Sutherland

I took a detour from the road to Durness to visit Kinlochbervie, the weather remaining warm and sunny. Where one might have expected a quaint fishing village, it seemed incongruous in the wild and craggy Sutherland landscape to encounter a huge harbour dominated by a massive fish-handling depot. Apparently, this is the reason the roads south of Kinlochbervie are so good – fish are packed here into large refrigerated lorries to be transported south and on to Europe.

Kinlochbervie is the highly industrious mainstay of deep-sea fishing in the far north-west. Developments began in 1964 to transform a small crofting community into a major European fishing harbour taking large trawlers. By 1990 the stocks of the most popular species were seriously reduced, which led to the introduction of fishing quotas, which in turn has posed major problems for the industry. In Scotland generally, the fishing industry has been in decline for some time, to be replaced by inshore lobster and prawn fishing and fish farming. The fleet of ships actually based here is small, and wandering around the almost empty port, this seemed to give Kinlochbervie a Spartan feel. However, many ships from the east of Scotland, and more recently the Faroes, land their catches here.

It boasts a very good hotel, but is hardly a tourist trap in itself, although it serves as a jumping-off point for the astonishingly beautiful coast north, including the magnificent Sandwood Bay. I had stayed in the hotel many years ago and was keen to see if it had changed, so rather than sample lunch in the Fisherman's Mission, I climbed the hill to the hotel.

Decisive forward planning had never been one of my strong points on this journey and that day was no exception. Over lunch in an otherwise empty bar, which looked only slightly less posh than I remembered, the only decision I made was to take advantage of the fine weather and make a picture of the harbour.

I felt that I needed some quiet time away from campsites and people, and a friend had mentioned a good place for wild camping north from Kinlochbervie. It had been a long day with an early start and I felt reluctant to drive much further, so I decided I would try to find it. I bought some coffee, eggs, bacon and sausages (no fresh fish!) in the local store and headed off to negotiate the sinuous and particularly narrow single-track road.

40

Camping, Sheigra, north-west Sutherland

It had turned quite nippy as I arrived across a muddy track at the extensive and deserted site, and I had only a little trouble finding a flat area to stop on. I made some coffee and was content to gaze mindlessly out to sea across an attractive beach. Sheigra is as far north as you can get by road on the west coast – ten miles south from Cape Wrath. I felt really alone for the first time in ages and the place had an air of silence and tranquillity that I enjoyed immensely. Blessed peace; I was just beginning to lapse into a snooze when, to my horror, a huge motorhome drew up right beside my wee van. I had hoped that the difficult approach to the site and its remoteness would deter the bigger motorhomes, but apparently not. Generally speaking, the further north you are in the Highlands the more chance you have of being alone. But as years go by, and with ever continuing improvements to roads, one has to travel much further to achieve this state of contentment. I fretted for half an hour, quite unreasonably annoyed and frustrated, wondering whether to move on, when the motorhome left.

A holiday in Scotland can be considerably more expensive than one in the Mediterranean, and while camping has always been attractive for some people, caravans and especially motorhomes are increasing in popularity, usually with older people. This is often to the frustration of local road users as these enormous (and expensive) vehicles attempt to navigate narrow roads and steep hills. I have heard also that locals in some areas resent the fact that it is possible to stock up with all necessary supplies in a supermarket in, say, Inverness and be completely self-sufficient for at least a week, so contributing nothing to the local tourist economy.

As the day wore on a few campers arrived in cars, and a smaller, older and more humble VW campervan arrived, selecting a position as far away from anybody else as possible. And later on still, just before dusk, a middle-aged couple arrived in an old Ford Fiesta and started to pitch a tent at a respectable distance. The windbreak was first to be erected.

The next morning, after a boiled egg and coffee, I nervously negotiated the mire-filled ruts off the grass and onto the track, emptied the waste tank and put fresh water in the van at the side of the nearby cemetery. Then, depositing the requested £4.00 in the honesty box at the side of the road I headed back towards Kinlochbervie.

41

Craft workers, Balnakeil, Durness

I rejoined the main road to Durness and, enjoying warm sunshine, was content to make slow progress. I stopped once or twice to make a picture, more in a sense of celebration of quite awesome landscape than with real purpose. So it was late morning when I arrived at Durness, where Muir stopped for lunch, and booked into the campsite. It was obviously a popular place because it was almost full, despite being enormous, with several family-sized tents. Nevertheless I managed to find a good pitch overlooking the sea and near to a water tap so that I could easily process some film.

In the afternoon, I heaved my camera and tripod on my back and cycled a couple of miles to the Balnakeil Craft Village. It's a disused military base that has played host to an eccentric township of craft and art activities since the late 1960s. The glum, flat-roofed buildings have been painted an assortment of colours and trees have been planted. Almost any village of reasonable size in the Highlands seems to have a craft shop of some description, catering for a tourist market, and these seem to be run almost exclusively by incomers looking for an alternative lifestyle. Throughout my journey I had seen numerous examples of really dreadful paintings of kitsch Highland scenes for sale in shops and cafes, but the standard at Balnakeil was high. There was a chocolate shop, an excellent bookshop and various craft studios. Craftshops seem to come and go with great regularity, and Balnakeil is no exception. There are some, however, that survive.

Without making a picture, I returned to the campsite and, irritated by my usual indecision, resolved to definitely photograph at Balnakeil the next day. The next morning I awoke to another glorious day at 6.30 a.m., and after a great deal of unnecessary pottering about I returned to the craft village.

Ludo is Belgian, Nicola is South African and they met in India. He is a wood-turner and repairs musical instruments and she is a ceramicist and painter. They had been resident together at Balnakeil for eight years. Although there was considerable passing trade in the summer, I wondered how they made much of a living up there, and how they had ended up so far north, a long way from a town of any reasonable size, where there would have been a much better market for their undoubted skills.

Nicola Poole and
Ludo van Muysen

42

Tractor, Strathnaver

From Durness I drove on along the north coast on a sublimely rocky coastline with occasional glimpses of pure white beaches. It was hot and sunny just as it had been for Muir, and in that desolate landscape (but not deserted, as in Muir's time), it did indeed seem 'sinister' at times. At least I did not have to endure plagues of horseflies as he did, but then he was in an open car and I was travelling faster. It took him two hours to get from the steep hill on the east bank of Loch Eriboll to Tongue, where he stopped for tea and I stopped for a bottle of lemonade.

Eventually I arrived at Bettyhill and decided to spend the night there. It's quite a sizeable sprawling village overlooked by a large white-painted hotel. Like most of the villages along the north coast it's not particularly attractive with an assortment of 1970s-style pebble-dashed terraced houses. The campsite was even less attractive: overgrown and boggy, with ghastly toilets and a general air of dilapidation. Returning to the village I bought a packet of cold ham and some tired-looking salad for my tea in the local store, wondering as usual why there was so little fresh local produce. Then a pint served by a chatty Polish girl in the friendly and vibrant hotel bar. Back to the dismal campsite and a young couple arrived with a tent at about 7.30 p.m. They had driven all the way from Liverpool that day and this was to be their first night in Scotland. How embarrassing.

It was an early-morning start and I headed south down Strathnaver thinking that I might photograph the landscape of the Clearances. The early-morning light was stunningly photogenic and it was hard to believe that this rich farming land was the location for the most infamous of the Clearances, conducted in the early nineteenth century by the notorious Patrick Sellar, on behalf of the Duke of Sutherland. Few Highland events have caused more controversy among historians. Muir attempted a balanced view, however it is clear where his sympathies lay:

'It is difficult now to understand why the Duke of Sutherland, who seems to have been a kind and enlightened man, should have rooted out a whole people with such barbarity. It was mainly, I think, because at that time intelligent men's minds were possessed by a dream of general wealth for society, which would be realised by adhering to the latest economic principles . . . [He] had no understanding of the Highland crofter who, though he lived more poorly than the cotton-spinner, lived also with more human satisfaction. [He] did not care very greatly what happened to the population if wealth could only be increased . . . it is this particular ideal of progress that has depopulated the Highlands and reduced them to the status of a backward region. They were robbed of their life by exactly the same process which built Glasgow.'

43

Noticeboard, Melvich

Retracing my route, I stopped at Farr church, just east of Bettyhill. It's now a museum principally commemorating the Clearances, but being a Sunday it was closed. The Sabbath is not as strictly observed here as it is on Lewis, but nevertheless most public buildings, except for hotels, are closed. Making a mental note to visit it next time I was up there, I drove on to Melvich. Muir spent his last night on mainland Scotland at the hotel here and he commented, 'That evening was the pleasantest of my whole journey.' Coincidentally, Muir too arrived on a Sunday at 8 p.m. in the evening and he had driven from Scourie to Melvich in one very long day. I decided to treat myself to a stay in the hotel. It was built in 1895; since then, unfortunately, they've built an accommodation block onto the side: a nasty 1980s flat-roofed affair, which they have had the good sense to screen from the road with mature trees. I presumed that the owners lived in the old part of the hotel.

The hotel was apparently staffed by only one young woman, who had an air of general confusion, and wasn't clear whether I was booking in or checking out. Having been given a dismal room, I fell asleep, to be woken shortly after by the same girl who said that the room was already booked and could I move to a different one. Later on I went into the bar for a drink to be served by the same bemused soul who was unsure what lager shandy was and then couldn't find the lemonade. I felt sorry for her and wondered how much she was paid to take the full responsibility for the place. I only met the owner once, when I checked out the next day. He was a Scotsman – and when I commented that it was unusual to find a Scotsman running a hotel in the Highlands, he said, 'I'm selling it.' I asked if it was to an Englishman, and he sighed wistfully, 'I hope so.' Maybe this accounted for the lugubrious air of the place, and I could only hope that he did manage to sell it to someone who might make improvements and train the staff better.

The van was parked across the road in a large empty lay-by beside public toilets and I took the opportunity to process some film with the easy availability of water. There was nobody about and I trotted backwards and forwards to the toilet, filling and emptying the tank without being disturbed. That was until the van was gradually surrounded by over a dozen vintage motor vehicles on a Sunday afternoon outing. That would never be allowed on Lewis.

Noticeboards in these rural areas have always seemed to me to be like a snapshot of a community. Sited in time and place, like the documentary photograph itself, they provide information for locals and visitors alike . . .

44

Passing place, Forsinard, Caithness

Despite the general air of malaise about the hotel, I had a fine breakfast the next morning, served by a thin elderly Highland woman with a dry and understated sense of humour. I wanted to take another diversion to look at the Flow Country so took the road south, just east of Melvich, intending one last night on mainland Scotland. The weather had changed to being heavy and dank, with the stubborn suggestion that this was not going to change for the rest of the day.

I drove as far as Forsinard, a tiny hamlet, but with a hotel, railway station and an adjoining visitor centre run by the Royal Society for the Protection of Birds. The Flow Country is an immense peatland, the largest expanse of blanket bog in Europe, sustaining a diversity of wildlife under the protection of the Forsinard Nature Reserve. Besides bird-watching, paradoxically, hunting, fishing and shooting are an important element of tourism here.

Perhaps unusually for the 1930s, Muir wrote ardently against hunting for sport, which he saw as a moral outrage and a further stage in the Clearances as large tracts of land were given over to grouse moors and deer-stalking. He maintained that Sir Walter Scott and Queen Victoria were to blame for 'this last disastrous phase': 'Scott sent the tourist wandering over Highland hills, and Queen Victoria built Balmoral.'

Muir felt that their influence was found in the stuffed heads of deer and '. . . pictures of slaughtered animals that disfigure the walls of Highland hotels'. In one hotel: '. . . this idea was carried out with such thoroughness that the walls of its dining-room looked like a shambles, they presented such an overwhelming array of bleeding birds, beasts and fishes. To find these abominations on the walls of Highland hotels, among a people of such delicacy in other things, is peculiarly revolting, and rubs in with superfluous force the fact that this is a land whose main contemporary industry is the shooting down of wild creatures; not production of any kind but wholesale destruction.'

Later in the day, I had a quick pint in the small, crowded public bar of the hotel (no taxidermy) and found a convenient spot to wild camp just off the road, a few miles north of Forsinard. While I was there a couple of men came out with rifles and took pot shots at a metal cut-out of a deer some distance away on the peatbog. Clearly there were other targets just as suitable, and as I watched I became intrigued by the variable meaning of 'Passing Place'.

Dundas Street, Stromness, Orkney

An early rise again the next day, quite excited by the prospect of leaving for Orkney, just as Muir must have been. It was to be the end of his journey and he had arranged to meet up with his wife Willa, and son Gavin, at Scapa. I decided to bypass Scrabster, where Muir took the ferry, and drive the extra 20 miles to Gill's Bay. It's less well known but is a cheaper and shorter crossing to St Margaret's Hope. After a pleasantly calm passage on a 35-year-old boat, I headed for Deerness, where Muir was born in 1887.

I bought some supplies at the Deerness Store, and asked if there was a campsite nearby, and the nice woman there said I could go down to the beach or to the community centre, where I could also use the toilets and showers. She kindly phoned the woman in charge but there was no reply. The campsite turned out to be the car park, where oddly there was a hook-up facility, but it was a bit public so I turned round and tried for the beach down a narrow road. I found a charming spot right next to the sands and decided to stay there, in splendid solitude, accompanied at a distance by only a couple of battered and apparently empty old caravans. The next day, I headed for Stromness.

Orkney represented Eden for Muir, and in 1934 he considered it to be 'the only desirable form of life . . . in all my journey through Scotland'. Its island community had been 'saved by being just outside the circumference of the industrial world, near enough to know about it, but too far off to be drawn into it'. Seventy years later, Orkney seemed to me to be a complete, self-contained and vigorous community; with a population of only 20,000, it boasts two newspapers and a radio station.

Stromness had a genteel quaintness about it, derived mainly from its narrow, meandering main street like a sinuous spine which remarkably still allows two-way traffic – although it does boast one traffic warden to facilitate the flow. It was also home to another great Orcadian writer, George Mackay Brown, who in 1951, at the age of 30, famously met Edwin Muir in the Stromness Hotel. I visited the bar and lounge frequently during my stay and it didn't look as if it had changed much since then.

From what I experienced and the evidence of the noticeboard outside the hotel, culture, especially music, is very much alive here. The Pier Arts Centre, which has long had a strong reputation, was in the process of being renovated and extended at a cost of £4.5 million.

I booked into the campsite at the Point of Ness, looking forward to staying in Orkney for several days.

46

Ring of Brodgar, Orkney

I spent most of the first few days in Orkney exploring the mainland and making contact with people I knew, including an old school friend, an engineer, who was an incomer of 25 years and whom I hadn't seen since I was at university. Besides that, I needed to catch up on processing and scanning film. It was approaching the end of the season and the campsite was due to close soon, as were some of the shops in the main street which were aimed principally at a seasonal market. Tourists to Orkney tend to be of the well-heeled type because of its remoteness and the expense of getting there. They go for the scenery, wildlife and historic Neolithic sites of Skara Brae, Maes Howe and so on. The oil industry, which came to Orkney in the 1970s bringing prosperity and the lowest unemployment rate in the Highlands and Islands, was sensibly corralled on the tiny island of Flotta. This meant that the rest of the Orkney islands are largely unspoilt for ecology and tourism.

Muir wrote that the Orkney islands 'are far less spectacular than the Western Highlands, and the tourist in search of the immediately picturesque will find little to repay him in them . . . nothing but bare low hills and ordinary farm-steadings, and would probably be bored in a few days'. However he goes on to say, 'There are innumerable signs . . . that these islands have been populated for several thousands of years and that one civilisation has followed another on them. Anyone who stays for long in Orkney is consequently bound to turn into an amateur archaeologist unless he has something more pressing to do.'

I had been intending to make a picture at Brodgar, and on my third day I woke at dawn to a clear and keen morning. As quickly as possible I packed away the bed and prayed that the light would hold while I drove the eight or so miles and set up the camera. It's always nail-biting stuff and the idea that serious landscape photography is relatively stress-free is a complete fallacy. Similarly, I had often in the past felt moved to acts of mild violence when it was suggested that I had been 'lucky with the light'.

Neolithic man left his mark monumentally on the landscape of Orkney. Besides celebrating unknown gods, perhaps he was also proclaiming his presence to the world then, and for millennia to come. So also did the Vikings who left runic inscriptions on the stones thousands of years later, to be followed by the nineteenth-century graffitists who carved deeply to announce that they too were there.

Who *was* J. Isbister, who left his humble legacy here in 1881?

47

Farming, Rousay

By now it was well into October and the weather was becoming noticeably chillier. I was glad that, back in Stornoway, I had purchased some warm pyjamas and a small fan heater for the van. One wild, full-mooned night at the Point of Ness, I woke to discover that the sea had risen over the wall and was steadily encroaching on the van. This necessitated a prompt relocation to the rear of the campsite, only just remembering to unplug the electrical hook-up while shivering in my pyjamas.

While in Orkney I had one commission to undertake for the Pier Arts Centre. The artist Ian Hamilton Finlay, who was a friend, had requested that I make a photograph of a huge inscribed slab of rock that he had installed on the highest point on Rousay, where he had worked as a roadman after the war. So, while I also made a photograph of the farming landscape, it was principally for this reason that I left the mainland and took the ferry from Tingwall over to Rousay. I discovered, with some anguish, that I had to reverse on to the small ferry, which I managed to do in a state of nervous tension. Neil Firth and Andrew Parkinson – or the 'nice boys at the Pier' as Ian had referred to them – had organised a local farmer to help by elevating me with camera on a palette at the front of his tractor, in order to get a better vantage point. He had left his native Yorkshire 30 years previously after a family dispute and just kept going until he reached Orkney. Having travelled through Scotland, he was astonished at the fine quality of the farmland there, and stayed on. The climate does not favour arable farming, however, and most farmers rear beef and dairy cattle. I think I saw more cattle in Orkney than almost the whole of my journey throughout the Highlands. The farming tradition in Orkney stretches back thousands of years and, unlike the Hebrides, there are few crofts, with most farming taking place on small owner-occupied farms. While the sea obviously has an immense influence, most of the fishing is inshore, and Orcadians have been described as 'farmers with boats', whereas in Shetland it's the reverse.

Orkney did not totally escape the Clearances, and the worst of these were on Rousay, carried out by General Frederick William Traill Burrows in the late nineteenth century. Muir briefly describes the 'Little General' – the most hated landlord in Orkney – in his *An Autobiography*. He was responsible 'by his exactions' for the Muir family moving from the Bu on neighbouring Wyre to a much inferior farm on the mainland.

The following day, having had a good meal in the pier restaurant the night before and then camping at the car park near to Yarso chambered cairn, I made a picture of Finlay's stone – with the farmer's generous help.

48

Ferry crew, Rousay

On the way over to Rousay the previous day, I had asked the skipper if I might make a picture of the crew, and he had agreed with laconic Orcadian friendliness. Then, that evening in the bar at Rousay pier, I met one of the ferry crew who, besides occasional work on the ferry, worked behind the bar and did a bit of cooking in the restaurant. He was a marine biologist who had worked for a Norwegian firm before being made redundant. The photograph was duly arranged for 2 p.m. at the pier the following day, which I intended to do after photographing Finlay's stone.

For many of the people I spoke to in Orkney, communications is, understandably, a major issue – particularly the ferry service, both between islands and to mainland Scotland. There are over 70 islands in the archipelago, and while the largest proportion of people live on the mainland, there are around 20 that are inhabited. I had thought a lot about island communities, their remoteness and logistical disadvantages, and yet the very fact of being an island creates, of itself, a contained community that seems more defined than anywhere on mainland Scotland.

Thinking about the two major island communities that I had visited, I was struck by similarities and differences. Lewis and Orkney have similar populations, but the latter is very much smaller in area and the community is therefore more compact – one might say close-knit. Besides that, Orkney has always had the advantage of much better farmland, and latterly oil, and therefore has been more prosperous. Both communities have been rightfully keen to preserve their heritage and distinct identities, but it seemed to me that Orkney has been much more enterprising, with a variety of small industries besides farming and fishing, such as jewellery and dairy produce, like Orkney ice cream and Orkney cheese. And there is a distillery, Highland Park – always a benefit for tourism as well as the economy.

Callum Flaws,
master
Martin Besant,
mate
Gordon Budge,
seaman
Euan Norquoy,
engineer

Waiting for the ferry to return to mainland Orkney, the weather became considerably worse and I spent some time in the small, recently refurbished heritage centre, which also boasted the cleanest public toilets I had so far encountered. As the ferry arrived in strong winds and rain, I convinced myself that I wasn't just a fair-weather photographer and determined to go ahead with the picture however bad the weather became. In the event, the same lens that had malfunctioned previously decided on a repeat performance, and in pouring rain I had to change lenses. Only three exposures were made. The subsequent crossing to the mainland gave me a taste of what winter weather must be like. The fully loaded ferry pitched and rolled and on several occasions the sea rose up over the bow and smashed into the van. I was thankful to reach Tingwall.

49

Jan Temple, The Bu, Wyre, Orkney

I had always intended that the culmination of my journey would be a visit to the Bu, where Muir spent arguably his happiest years as a child between the ages of two and nine. His time here was to shape his view of Orkney as Eden, and a fifth of his autobiography is devoted to those seven short years.

Neil and Andrew at the Pier Arts Centre provided me with a telephone number for the Bu and I phoned to make an appointment; after some initial reticence, a time was agreed. So the following day, I returned to Tingwall to cross to Rousay and then five minutes over to Wyre. It's tiny: about two miles by one and has a population of about 20. In Muir's day the population was substantial enough to support a school, which now, remarkably for such a small place, is a heritage centre – albeit humble and unstaffed.

The 100-acre farm of the Bu is now home to Jan Temple and her husband Clive, who bought it about seven years previously. They were originally from Kent and moved to Orkney for what they saw as a better quality of life. Jan is a part-time care assistant on Rousay and her husband Clive works for social services on the mainland, so really they are crofters (who very rarely make a living from the land itself) and are learning about farming. They were saving up to buy a tractor. Most of the land isn't cultivated and I didn't see any sheep or cows although they keep pigs, hens and geese. The cottage was much as it would have been in Muir's day, and Jan and Clive live in a tiny part of the old byre at the back. They planned to renovate the cottage – a major undertaking because of its poor condition, although it is watertight with three-foot-thick stone walls. A neighbour had told them that they should just pull it down; that they could have a new kit house in two months, and much more cheaply. I thought it was great that they were persevering – particularly since it was clear they weren't rich. Of the seven small farms on Wyre only two were run by indigenous Orcadians. I asked her about Orcadians viewing her as an incomer and she said that she hadn't had a problem in terms of jobs, but she knew people who had, and who had left. Not surprisingly, a main issue for her in Orkney is transport and its expense – particularly petrol and ferries. This made me wonder why they had chosen to live in such an inaccessible place with no amenities, dependent almost daily on ferries and cars.

I suppose it most clearly represented for me the huge paradox between the desire for remoteness and the need for accessibility.

50

The Bu, Wyre, Orkney

I had intended to stay overnight on Wyre, but given that the weather was as flat and dull as the island, I decided to take the 3.30 p.m. ferry back to the mainland. That gave me two hours to make a picture of the Bu and I set up the camera near the heritage centre.

'Eden' was not my first response to this treeless and rather dreary island. But to Muir as an imaginative young boy who as yet knew nothing else, and as an older man who had experienced the depression of Glasgow's industrial squalor, it must have seemed so. My computer spell-check seems in sympathy with Muir though: it does not recognise 'Orcadian' and suggests instead 'Arcadian'.

I waited almost an hour and a half for the light to improve and in the end I made a picture anyway before moving down to the pier. Just as I was reversing onto the ferry again, the sun suddenly flashed through the low cloud . . .

I stayed in Orkney for a total of 11 days, which was the longest I spent in any one place. It was the end of my journey as it had been Muir's 70 years previously; just as he had met his family there, I was looking forward to meeting mine back in Edinburgh.

I was in the ferry queue at Stromness for the *Hamnavoe* at 10 a.m. and arrived at Scrabster at 12.30 p.m. After filling up with petrol at Thurso (cheaper than in Orkney), I pointed the van south in the direction of the A9. Having scarcely seen a tree for almost a fortnight, it was a revelation to see that autumn had definitely announced itself with a glorious display of rich colour.

On the road south I contemplated what I had learnt from my impressions of the Highlands. I had always understood that Scotland as a whole consisted of various regional identities, but I was struck also by the considerable diversity within the Highlands and Islands themselves. I found it difficult to ascertain a homogenous identity. My journey had presented me with a litany of tensions, conundrums and paradoxes.

How is the tension to be resolved between the need to safeguard traditional Highland culture while encouraging economic progress? How can it be preserved while welcoming those who wish to visit – and embracing those who wish to settle? What's the solution to the conundrum of the need for sustainable energy versus the conservation of the immediate environment and landscape? How can a sense of history and heritage be encouraged without sentimentalism and nostalgia? And can the Scottish Highlands really claim a kindred identity?

Let Muir have the last word: 'I had to admit to myself that I had seen a great number of things, but no thing, and to fall back on the conclusion that nationality is real and yet indefinable, and that it can be grasped at most in history, which means that it cannot really be grasped at all . . .'